Contents

Published by CGP

ISBN: 978 1 78294 521 5

www.cgpbooks.co.uk
Printed by Elanders Ltd, Newcastle upon Tyne.
Clipart from Corel®
Text, design, layout and original illustrations © Coordination Group Publications Ltd. (CGP) 2016
All rights reserved.

Topic C1

Topic C1 — Particles

Page 1 — States of Matter

Warm-up

Particles in liquids are held in fixed positions by strong forces.

1   When a physical change occurs, there are no new substances made *[1 mark]*. During a chemical change, the atoms rearrange themselves to form new products *[1 mark]*.

2 a)   Any two from e.g.: Particles are not solid spheres, they are atoms, ions, or molecules. / The model doesn't show the size of the particle. / The model doesn't show the space between particles. / The model doesn't show forces between particles, so their strength is unknown.
[2 marks — 1 mark for each correct answer]

  b)   Particles in liquids are constantly moving with a random motion *[1 mark]*, whereas particles in solids vibrate around fixed positions *[1 mark]*.

Page 2 — The History of the Atom

1 a)   The model described the atom as a cloud of positive charge *[1 mark]* which contained smaller, negatively charged particles called electrons *[1 mark]*.

  b) i) Most of the particles passed straight through the foil and very few were deflected back *[1 mark]*.

    ii) A small, positively charged nucleus is found at the centre of the atom *[1 mark]* and is surrounded by a cloud of negative electrons *[1 mark]*. Most of the atom is empty space *[1 mark]*.

  c)   Rutherford's model stated that a cloud of electrons surrounded the nucleus *[1 mark]*. Bohr's model showed that electrons exist in fixed orbitals/shells *[1 mark]*.

  d)   Older models fitted the evidence that was available at the time *[1 mark]*. As more experiments were carried out, new evidence was obtained which was used to modify the current theories and produce new models *[1 mark]*.

  e)   E.g. errors can be checked by other scientists before the studies are published in journals *[1 mark]*.

Page 3 — The Atom

1 a)

Particle	Relative Mass	Charge
Proton	1	+1
Neutron	1	0
Electron	0.0005	−1

[1 mark]

  b)   Neutrons and protons *[1 mark]*. Neutrons have no charge and protons are positively charged, so the nucleus has an overall positive charge *[1 mark]*.

2 a)   C *[1 mark]*

  b)   Electrons move around the nucleus in electron shells/orbitals. These electron shells cover a lot of space *[1 mark]*. The volume of these shells determine the size of the atom and so, the atomic radius *[1 mark]*.

Page 4 — Atoms, Isotopes and Ions

1 a)   The atomic number shows that carbon has 6 protons *[1 mark]*.

  b)   Number of neutrons = 20 − 10 = **10** *[1 mark]*

  c)   9 *[1 mark]*

2 a)   The atom gains one or more electrons *[1 mark]*.

  b)   Number of electrons = 12 − 2 = **10** *[1 mark]*

An ion with a 2+ charge has lost two electrons.

Answers

GCSE Chemistry

For OCR Gateway (Grade 9-1)

Exam Practice Answer Book

Topic C2

3 a) Isotopes are different forms of the same element. They have the same number of protons but a different number of neutrons / Isotopes have the same atomic number but a different mass number *[1 mark]*.

b) Br–79: Number of neutrons = 79 – 35 = **44**
Br–81: Number of neutrons = 81 – 35 = **46**
[1 mark for both correct]

Topic C2 — Elements, Compounds and Mixtures

Page 5 — The Periodic Table

1 a) Mendeleev left gaps because he wanted to keep elements with similar properties in the same vertical groups *[1 mark]*.

b) The properties of new elements that were discovered in the years after Mendeleev published his table matched his predictions for the properties of the elements that would fill the gaps in the table *[1 mark]*.

c) When protons were discovered, scientists were able to calculate the atomic number of each element *[1 mark]*. When the elements were arranged in order of increasing atomic number, they matched the order Mendeleev had put them in *[1 mark]*.

Page 6 — Electron Shells

1 C *[1 mark]*
The electronic structure of neon is 2.8, which means there are 8 electrons in its outer shell.

2 a) 2.8.6 *[1 mark]*
b)

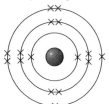

[1 mark]

3 The group number tells you how many electrons are in the outer shell, so magnesium has 2 outer shell electrons *[1 mark]*. The period number tells you how many electron shells the atom has in total, so magnesium has three shells *[1 mark]*. All the shells apart from the outer shell will be filled (the first holds 2 electrons and the second holds 8) *[1 mark]*. So the electronic structure of magnesium must be 2.8.2 *[1 mark]*.

Pages 7-8 — Ionic Compounds

1 When sodium bromide is a solid, its ions are fixed in place, so they can't move *[1 mark]*. When it is in solution, the ions separate and are free to move and carry an electric charge *[1 mark]*.

2 a) +1 *[1 mark]*
The potassium atom loses its single outer shell electron to form an ion with a stable electronic structure. Electrons have a negative charge, so losing one electron changes the overall charge from 0 to +1.

b) 2.8.8 *[1 mark]*

3

[1 mark for correct electronic structure of fluoride ions, 1 mark for correct electronic structure of calcium ions, 1 mark for correct charges on calcium ion and fluoride ions.]

4 a) The charges on the ions that make up an ionic compound must always balance to give an overall charge of zero *[1 mark]*. There's one sulfide ion for every 2+ magnesium ion, so the charge on the sulfide ion must be 2– *[1 mark]*.

b) i) The ions in an ionic solid are held together by strong electrostatic forces of attraction *[1 mark]*. A large amount of energy is needed to overcome these forces, so ionic solids have high melting points *[1 mark]*.

ii) The ions in magnesium sulfide have greater charges than the ions in sodium chloride / magnesium ions have a 2+ charge and sulfide ions a 2– charge, while sodium ions have a 1+ charge and chloride ions a 1– charge *[1 mark]*. This means that the ions in magnesium sulfide are more strongly attracted to each other than the ions in sodium chloride *[1 mark]*. More energy is needed to separate them, so magnesium sulfide has a higher melting point *[1 mark]*.

5 Barium is more reactive than strontium *[1 mark]*. Barium is lower down the group than strontium, which means it has more electron shells, so its outer electrons are further away from the nucleus *[1 mark]*. This means barium's outer electrons will be easier to remove, so barium will be more reactive *[1 mark]*.

Pages 9-10 — Simple Molecules

1 a) i) ball and stick model *[1 mark]*
ii) displayed formula *[1 mark]*

b) E.g. the diagram shows gaps between the atoms, but in reality these spaces are filled by the atoms' electron clouds. *[1 mark for any sensible limitation of ball and stick models.]*

2 a) In a covalent bond, each atom donates one electron to the bond to make a shared pair of electrons *[1 mark]*. This increases the number of outer shell electrons in both atoms by one *[1 mark]*. Each atom forms enough covalent bonds to give it a full outer shell of electrons, which is more stable than an incomplete shell *[1 mark]*.

b) Neon has a full outer shell of electrons, so it can't achieve a more stable electronic structure by sharing electrons in covalent bonds *[1 mark]*.

3 A silicon atom has four outer shell electrons, so it needs another four to have a full outer shell *[1 mark]*. So a silicon atom will form four covalent bonds *[1 mark]*.

4

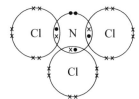

[1 mark for correctly showing three chlorine-nitrogen bonds as shared pairs of electrons, 1 mark for showing one additional pair of electrons on the nitrogen atom and three on each chlorine atom.]

5 Hashim is wrong. Simple molecular substances have low melting and boiling points *[1 mark]*. To melt or boil a simple molecular substance, you only need to overcome the intermolecular forces which hold the molecules together *[1 mark]*. Intermolecular forces are weak, so they can be broken with a small amount of energy *[1 mark]*.

Page 11 — Giant Covalent Structures and Fullerenes

1 a) i) graphite *[1 mark]*
ii) fullerene *[1 mark]*

b) Both structures have delocalised electrons *[1 mark]*, which can move and carry a charge *[1 mark]*.

c) Graphite (the structure in diagram A) should have the higher melting point *[1 mark]*. It has a giant covalent structure, so to melt it you need to break the strong covalent bonds holding the atoms together *[1 mark]*. Fullerenes are molecular, so to melt them you only need to break the weak intermolecular forces holding the molecules together *[1 mark]*.

d) E.g. diamond: OR graphene:

[1 mark for correct name, 1 mark for correct structure.]

Page 12 — Nanoparticles

1   A *[1 mark]*

2 a) E.g. fullerenes could be used to deliver drugs directly to individual cells, because fullerenes are more easily absorbed into the body than larger particles. / Silver nanoparticles can be added to the fibres used to make surgical masks and wound dressings, because silver nanoparticles have antibacterial properties.
[1 mark for a medical use of nanoparticles, 1 mark for relating the given use to properties of nanoparticles.]

b) Nanomedicines are a new form of medicine, so they need to be tested *[1 mark]* for unexpected or harmful side effects before they can be considered safe to use *[1 mark]*.

3   E.g. the surface area to volume ratio *[1 mark]* of nanoparticles is much higher than that of larger particles *[1 mark]*. This gives nanoparticles different qualities because a much greater proportion of their atoms are available to interact with other substances *[1 mark]*.

Page 13 — Polymers

Warm-up
Polymers are **long** molecules. They are formed from **small** molecules called **monomers**. Polymers are often referred to as **plastics**. Polymers contain **covalent** bonds, but often behave very differently from simple **molecular** substances.

1   How to grade your answer:

Level 0:   There is no relevant information. *[No marks]*

Level 1:   Polymer Y is identified as having stronger bonds between the polymer chains than polymer Z, and there is a suggestion of the nature of the different bonding between the chains in the two polymers. *[1 to 2 marks]*

Level 2:   Polymer Y is identified as having stronger bonds between the polymer chains than polymer Z. There is a suggestion of the nature of the different bonding between the chains in the two polymers and a brief description of how these differences can affect the properties of polymers. *[3 to 4 marks]*

Level 3:   Polymer Y is identified as having stronger bonds between the polymer chains than polymer Z. There is a suggestion of the nature of the different bonding between the chains in the two polymers. Each of the differences in their properties is clearly explained in terms of the differences in bonding between the chains. *[5 to 6 marks]*

Here are some points your answer may include:
The polymers are both made of the same two elements, so the differences in their properties are likely to be due to differences in their structure and bonding.
The differences in the properties of the polymers suggest that the polymer chains in polymer Y are held together by stronger bonds than the chains in polymer Z.
The chains of polymer Z are probably only held together by weak intermolecular forces, while the chains of polymer Y are probably linked by stronger covalent bonds/crosslinks. Covalent bonds are stronger and require more energy to break them than intermolecular forces. This explains why polymer Y has a higher melting point than polymer Z.
The covalent crosslinks in polymer Y hold the polymer chains in fixed positions in relation to each other. This explains why polymer Y is rigid and does not stretch.
The weak intermolecular forces in polymer Z allow the polymer chains to slide over each other. This explains why polymer Z is flexible and easily stretched.

Page 14 — Properties of Materials

1 a) Iodine monochloride *[1 mark]*, because fluoroethane and iodine monochloride are both simple molecular substances, which generally have lower melting and boiling points than polymers or ionic compounds *[1 mark]*.

b) E.g. bromine can form both ionic and simple molecular compounds *[1 mark]*. Ionic compounds can conduct electricity when they are molten or in solution, but simple molecular compounds don't conduct electricity *[1 mark]*.

2   No. The properties of a material are determined by its structure and bonding as well as the atoms it contains *[1 mark]*. White phosphorus is likely to have a low melting point *[1 mark]*, because to melt it you only need to break the weak intermolecular forces holding the molecules together *[1 mark]*. Black phosphorus is likely to have a high melting point *[1 mark]*, because to melt it you have to break the strong covalent bonds holding the atoms together *[1 mark]*.

Page 15 — Metals

Warm-up
good conductor of heat, high melting point, malleable, crystal structure when solid

1   A *[1 mark]*

2 a)

[1 mark for showing positive metal ions, 1 mark for showing free electrons, 1 mark for correct labels.]

b) i) Metals usually have high melting points because a large amount of energy is needed to overcome the strong electrostatic attraction *[1 mark]* between the positive ions and the delocalised 'sea' of electrons *[1 mark]*.

ii) The delocalised electrons are free to move *[1 mark]*, so they can carry a charge through the solid metal *[1 mark]*.

Pages 16-17 — States, Structure and Bonding

1   B *[1 mark]*

2   The first change seen would be bromine freezing from a red-brown liquid to a red-brown metallic solid *[1 mark]*. The next change would be mercury freezing from a silvery metallic liquid to a silvery metallic solid *[1 mark]*. Near the end of the experiment, the fluorine would condense from a pale yellow gas to a bright yellow liquid *[1 mark]*. The rubidium would start out as a silvery-white metallic solid, and remain unchanged throughout *[1 mark]*.

3 a) Leonie is unlikely to be correct. Substance 2 conducts electricity, but substance 4 does not, which suggests they have different structures *[1 mark]*.

b) Jing is likely to be correct. Ionic compounds don't conduct electricity when they are solid, but they do when they are molten or in solution *[1 mark]*.

c) i) substance 1 *[1 mark]*

ii) It suggests that substance 1 has a simple molecular structure *[1 mark]*, as simple molecular substances tend to have very low melting and boiling points *[1 mark]*.

Page 18 — Purity

1 The scientific definition of a pure substance is one that contains only one element or compound *[1 mark]*. Although it is labelled 'pure', Stanley's spring water is likely to contain traces of other compounds or elements as well as water molecules (so it will not fit the scientific definition of 'pure water') *[1 mark]*.

2 The boiling point of an impure substance is higher than the boiling point of the pure substance *[1 mark]* so the pure sample will be the one with the lower boiling point *[1 mark]*.

3 A *[1 mark]*

Impurities lower the melting point of a substance, so an impure sample of ammonium nitrate would melt below 170 °C, but impure citric acid would already have melted by the time the temperature reached 156 °C. A mixture of the two powdered substances would melt over a range of temperatures, starting at or below the melting point of citric acid.

Pages 19-21 — Purification Techniques

1 a) i) A: fractionating column *[1 mark]*

ii) B: condenser *[1 mark]*

b) i) fractional distillation *[1 mark]*

ii) A mixture of liquids *[1 mark]* with similar boiling points *[1 mark]*.

iii) E.g. electric heater / water bath *[1 mark]*

You don't get the mark here for naming any heating device with an open flame (like a Bunsen burner).

2 How to grade your answer:

Level 0: There is no relevant information. *[No marks]*

Level 1: A method is described which would allow you to obtain a pure sample of only one of the components. *[1 to 2 marks]*

Level 2: A method is described which would allow you to obtain pure samples of both components, but some details may be missing or incorrect. *[3 to 4 marks]*

Level 3: A method is described clearly and in full, which would allow you to obtain pure samples of both components. *[5 to 6 marks]*

Here are some points your answer may include:

Mix the powder with water. This will dissolve the potassium iodide, but not the barium sulfate.

Filter the mixture through a filter paper in a funnel.

The solid barium sulfate will be left in the filter paper.

The solid barium sulfate can be washed with water to remove any traces of potassium iodide and then dried.

The remaining liquid part of the mixture will be a solution of potassium iodide.

To obtain pure potassium iodide from this solution, you can use crystallisation.

Gently heat the solution in an evaporation dish until some of the water has evaporated / until crystals start to form.

Allow the solution to cool, then filter out the crystals.

Dry the crystals by leaving them in a warm place / using a drying oven / using a desiccator.

3 a) Filtration *[1 mark]* would separate sodium chloride and ethanol, as the liquid ethanol would flow through the filter paper, leaving behind the solid sodium chloride *[1 mark]*. However, a mixture of sodium chloride and water is a solution, so both the water and dissolved sodium chloride would pass through the filter paper *[1 mark]*.

b) E.g. distillation *[1 mark]* would separate both mixtures, as in both cases the liquid component would evaporate and leave behind the solid sodium chloride *[1 mark]*.

4 The difference in the boiling points of cyclohexane and cyclopentane is quite large, so you could separate them using simple distillation *[1 mark]*. But the boiling points of cyclohexane and ethyl ethanoate are quite similar, so you would need to use fractional distillation to separate them *[1 mark]*.

Pages 22-23 — Chromatography

1 D *[1 mark]*

2 a) There is only one peak, which suggests there is only one substance, not a mixture of substances *[1 mark]*.

b) The time taken for the chemical being analysed to travel through the equipment / reach the detector *[1 mark]*.

3 a) The chromatogram suggests there are two components in the mixture, as the mixture has separated into two spots *[1 mark]*.

b) Distance from baseline to spot B = 0.8 cm

Distance from baseline to solvent front = 4.0 cm

[1 mark for both distances correctly measured]

R_f = distance travelled by solute ÷ distance travelled by solvent

= 0.8 ÷ 4.0 = **0.2** *[1 mark]*

c) Olivia could re-run the experiment with spots of the pure chemicals alongside the mixture / analyse samples of each of the pure chemicals using paper chromatography, under the same conditions as the mixture *[1 mark]*. The R_f values of / distance travelled by each spot in the mixture will match the R_f values of / distance travelled by the pure sample of the component responsible for that spot *[1 mark]*.

Page 24 — Relative Masses

1 C *[1 mark]*

2 M_r of $Zn(CN)_2$

= A_r of Zn + (2 × (A_r of C + A_r of N))

= 65.4 + (2 × (12.0 + 14.0))

= 65.4 + (2 × 26.0)

= 65.4 + 52.0 = **117.4**

[2 marks for the correct answer, otherwise 1 mark for writing a correct expression that could be used to calculate the M_r of $Zn(CN)_2$]

3 M_r of $Ba(NO_3)_2$

= A_r of Ba + (2 × (A_r of N + (3 × A_r of O)))

= 137.3 + (2 × (14.0 + (3 × 16.0)))

= 137.3 + (2 × (14.0 + 48.0))

= 137.3 + (2 × 62.0)

= 137.3 + 124.0 = **261.3**

[2 marks for the correct answer, otherwise 1 mark for writing a correct expression that could be used to calculate the M_r of $Ba(NO_3)_2$]

4 M_r of X_2O_3 = (2 × A_r of X) + (3 × A_r of O)

So 159.6 = (2 × A_r of X) + (3 × 16.0)

159.6 = (2 × A_r of X) + 48.0

2 × A_r of X = 159.6 – 48.0 = 111.6

so A_r of X = 111.6 ÷ 2 = **55.8**

[3 marks for the correct answer, otherwise 1 mark for a correct equation for the M_r of X_2O_3 and 1 mark for substituting in values of M_r of X_2O_3 and A_r of O to give an equation which could be rearranged to give the A_r of X.]

Topic C3

Pages 25-26 — Molecular and Empirical Formulas

Warm-up

oxygen: 2, carbon: 5, nitrogen: 0, hydrogen: 10

1   D *[1 mark]*

2 a) $H_2S_2O_6$ *[1 mark]*

  b)   The largest number that goes into all the numbers in the molecular formula exactly is 2:

        H: $2 \div 2 = 1$

        S: $2 \div 2 = 1$

        O: $6 \div 2 = 3$

        So the empirical formula is HSO_3 *[1 mark]*

3   The largest number that goes into both 10 and 14 exactly is 2:

        B: $10 \div 2 = 5$ H: $14 \div 2 = 7$

        So the empirical formula of decaborane is B_5H_7 *[1 mark]*.

4     $10 = 5 \times 2$, so to get from the empirical formula to the molecular formula, multiply all the numbers of atoms by 2:

        $6 \times 2 = 12$, $5 \times 2 = 10$ and $2 \times 2 = 4$.

        So the empirical formula is $C_{12}H_{10}O_4$

        [2 marks for the correct answer, otherwise 1 mark for showing the empirical formula should be multiplied by 2.]

5   Emmy is incorrect, e.g. because she not has divided the numbers in the molecular formula by the largest number that will go into both exactly / she has divided both numbers in the formula by 4, but she could have divided by $8 / 8 \div 8 = 1$ and $16 \div 8 = 2$, so the empirical formula is CH_2 *[1 mark]*.

6   Relative mass of empirical formula is

        $(2 \times A_r \text{ of C}) + (A_r \text{ of H}) + (A_r \text{ of F}) = (2 \times 12.0) + 1.0 + 19.0$

        $= 24.0 + 1.0 + 19.0 = 44.0$

        M_r of Q $\div M_r$ of empirical formula $= 132.0 \div 44.0 = 3$

        So to get the molecular formula, multiply the numbers of atoms in the empirical formula by 3:

        molecular formula $= C_6H_3F_3$

        [3 marks for correct answer, otherwise 1 mark for finding the relative mass of the empirical formula and 1 mark for dividing the relative mass of the molecular formula by the relative mass of the empirical formula.]

Topic C3 — Chemical Reactions

Page 27 — Conservation of Mass

1   Disagree. The extra mass came from the oxygen in the air becoming part of the solid product / atoms can't be created during a reaction *[1 mark]*.

2 a)   The total mass of the flask and its contents will decrease over the course of the reaction *[1 mark]* as one of the products is hydrogen gas, which is lost from the flask *[1 mark]*.

  b)   The total mass of the flask and its contents would stay the same over the course of the reaction *[1 mark]* as the reaction is happening in a closed system / any hydrogen gas evolved wouldn't be able to escape, so no reactants are lost *[1 mark]*.

Page 28 — Chemical Formulas

Warm-up

+2 = calcium, barium, magnesium   +1 = lithium, sodium

−1 = iodine, chlorine   −2 = sulfur, selenium

1   A *[1 mark]*

2   +3 *[1 mark]*

Each chloride ion has a charge of −1. There are three chloride ions for every one iron ion, so for each iron ion, there's a charge of (−1 × 3 =) −3 from chloride ions. Ionic compounds are neutral, so the iron ion must have a charge of +3 to balance the charge from the chloride ions.

3   C *[1 mark]*

Pages 29-31 — Chemical Equations

For all the equations in the answers below (and any other 'balanced equation' questions), you'll get the marks if your equation is equivalent to the answer given — in other words, if you've got the same equation, but with all the numbers of moles multiplied by the same number.

1   C *[1 mark]*

2     $CaCO_3\textbf{(s)} + 2HNO_3\textbf{(aq)} \rightarrow Ca(NO_3)_2\textbf{(aq)} + H_2O\textbf{(l)} + CO_2\textbf{(g)}$

        [1 mark for correct left-hand side, 1 mark for correct right-hand side.]

3     $4Na + O_2 \rightarrow 2Na_2O$

        [2 marks for all formulas correct and a correctly-balanced equation, otherwise 1 mark for correct formulas in an unbalanced equation.]

4 a)   A solid precipitate of AgCl is formed *[1 mark]*.

  b) $Ag^+_{(aq)} + Cl^-_{(aq)} \rightarrow AgCl_{(s)}$

        [2 marks for all formulas correct and a correctly-balanced equation, otherwise 1 mark for correct formulas in an unbalanced equation.]

5 a)   That the substance is dissolved in water / aqueous *[1 mark]*.

  b) $2Al_{(s)} + 3H_2SO_{4\,(aq)} \rightarrow Al_2(SO_4)_{3\,(aq)} + 3H_{2\,(g)}$

        [2 marks for correct answer, otherwise 1 mark for some correct working.]

  c)   Fizzing / bubbles of gas being given off *[1 mark]* as hydrogen gas is produced *[1 mark]*.

You would also get the marks for saying that you'd see the size of the aluminium decreasing as the reaction progressed, as it reacted to form soluble aluminium sulfate.

6     $S + 6HNO_3 \rightarrow H_2SO_4 + 6NO_2 + 2H_2O$

        [2 marks for correct answer, otherwise 1 mark for some correct working.]

7     $2K_{(s)} + Br_{2\,(aq)} \rightarrow 2KBr_{(aq)}$

        [2 marks for all formulas correct and a correctly-balanced equation, otherwise 1 mark for correct formulas in an unbalanced equation.]

8 a) $Zn_{(s)} + Sn^{2+}_{(aq)} \rightarrow Zn^{2+}_{(aq)} + Sn_{(s)}$

        [1 mark for correct left-hand side, 1 mark for correct right-hand side.]

  b) $Zn \rightarrow Zn^{2+} + 2e^-$ *[1 mark]*

        $Sn^{2+} + 2e^- \rightarrow Sn$ *[1 mark]*

9 a) $2Ag^+_{(aq)} + Cu_{(s)} \rightarrow 2Ag_{(s)} + Cu^{2+}_{(aq)}$

        [1 mark for correct left-hand side, 1 mark for correct right-hand side.]

  b) $2AgNO_{3\,(aq)} + Cu_{(s)} \rightarrow 2Ag_{(s)} + Cu(NO_3)_{2\,(aq)}$

        [2 marks for all formulas correct and a correctly-balanced equation, otherwise 1 mark for correct formulas in an unbalanced equation.]

To answer this question, all you have to do is balance the charges on all the positive ions with negatively charged nitrate ions.

Pages 32-33 — Moles

1   D *[1 mark]*

2     $M_r(C_9H_8O_4) = (12.0 \times 9) + (1.0 \times 8) + (16.0 \times 4)$

        $= \textbf{180}$ *[1 mark]*

        mass = moles $\times M_r = 12.4 \times 180 = \textbf{2232 g}$ *[1 mark]*

3   no. molecules = moles × Avogadro's constant

        $= 7 \times 6.022 \times 10^{23} = 4.22 \times 10^{24}$ *[1 mark]*

        In 1 molecule of ammonia, there are 4 atoms, so in 4.22×10^{24} molecules of ammonia, there must be

        $4.22 \times 10^{24} \times 4 = \textbf{1.69} \times \textbf{10}^{\textbf{25}}$ **atoms** *[1 mark]*

4   From top to bottom:

        $1 \div (6.022 \times 10^{23}) = \textbf{1.7} \times \textbf{10}^{\textbf{-24}}$ *[1 mark]*

        14 *[1 mark]*

        $27 \div (6.022 \times 10^{23}) = \textbf{4.5} \times \textbf{10}^{\textbf{-23}}$ *[1 mark]*

        18 *[1 mark]*

        $48 \div (6.022 \times 10^{23}) = \textbf{8.0} \times \textbf{10}^{\textbf{-23}}$ *[1 mark]*

Topic C3

5 a) $(1.2044 \times 10^{25}) \div (6.022 \times 10^{23}) = $ **20 moles** *[1 mark]*

b) $(9.27 \times 10^{-23}) \times (6.022 \times 10^{23}) = 55.82...$ *[1 mark]*
This atomic mass is closest to iron, so the element must be **iron** *[1 mark]*.

6 a) $M_r = $ mass $\div$ moles $= 343.35 \div 3.5 = $ **98.1** *[1 mark]*

b) 65% of 98.1 $= (98.1 \div 100) \times 65 = 63.765$ *[1 mark]*
Moles of O in 63.765 g $= 63.765 \div 16 = 3.98...$
$= $ **4 moles** *[1 mark]*

c) Mass of 1 mole of S $= 32.1$ g
Mass of 4 moles of O $= 16.0 \times 4 = 64$ g
Mass of H in 1 mole of acid $= 98.1 - 64 - 32.1 = 2$ g *[1 mark]*
Moles of H in 2 g $= 2 \div 1.0 = 2$
So ratio of S : O : H $= 1 : 4 : 2$ *[1 mark]*,
so formula $= $ **H_2SO_4** *[1 mark]*

Pages 34-35 — Calculating Masses

Warm-up
1) decrease   2) increase   3) not change

1 a) magnesium *[1 mark]*

b) The hydrochloric acid is the limiting reagent *[1 mark]* as there is magnesium metal left over in the reaction, showing that it's in excess *[1 mark]*.

2    $M_r(C_2H_4) = (12.0 \times 2) + (1.0 \times 4) = 28.0$
moles $= $ mass $\div M_r = 53.2 \div 28.0 = 1.90$ moles *[1 mark]*
From the reaction equation, 1 mole of C_2H_4 produces 1 mole of CH_3CH_2OH, so 1.90 moles of C_2H_4 will produce 1.90 moles of CH_3CH_2OH.
$M_r(CH_3CH_2OH) = 12.0 + (1.0 \times 3) + 12.0 + (1.0 \times 2) + 16.0 + 1.0 = 46.0$
mass $= $ moles $\times M_r = 1.90 \times 46.0 = $ **87.4 g** *[1 mark]*

3 a) $M_r(O_2) = 16.0 \times 2 = 32.0$
moles $= $ mass $\div M_r = 128 \div 32.0 = 4.00$ moles *[1 mark]*
From the reaction equation, 7 moles of O_2 produce 6 moles of H_2O, so 4.00 moles of O_2 will produce $((4.00 \div 7) \times 6) = 3.42...$ moles of H_2O.
$M_r(H_2O) = (1.0 \times 2) + 16.0 = 18.0$
mass $= $ moles $\times M_r = 3.42... \times 18.0 = $ **61.7 g**
[1 mark for a correct answer, 1 mark for giving answer to 3 significant figures.]

b) $M_r(CO_2) = 12.0 + (16.0 \times 2) = 44.0$
4.4 tonnes $= 4.4 \times 1\,000\,000 = 4\,400\,000$ g
moles $= $ mass $\div M_r$
$= 4\,400\,000 \div 44.0 = 100\,000$ moles *[1 mark]*
For every 4 moles of CO_2 produced, 2 moles of ethane are burnt. So if 100 000 moles of CO_2 are produced, $((100\,000 \div 4) \times 2 =) 50\,000$ moles of ethane are burnt.
$M_r(C_2H_6) = (12.0 \times 2) + (1.0 \times 6) = 30.0$
mass $= $ moles $\times M_r = 50\,000 \times 30.0 = 1\,500\,000$ g
1 500 000 g $= 1\,500\,000 \div 1\,000\,000 = $ **1.5 tonnes** *[1 mark]*

4 a) $M_r((NH_2)_2CO) = 2 \times (14.0 + 1.0 + 1.0) + 12.0 + 16.0 = 60.0$
120.6 tonnes $= 120.6 \times 1\,000\,000 = 120\,600\,000$ g
moles $= $ mass $\div M_r$
$= 120\,600\,000 \div 60.0 = 2\,010\,000$ moles *[1 mark]*
From the reaction equation, 1 mole of $(NH_2)_2CO$ is made from 1 mole of CO_2, so making 2 010 000 moles of $(NH_2)_2CO$ will require 2 010 000 moles of CO_2.
$M_r(CO_2) = 12.0 + (16.0 \times 2) = 44.0$
mass $= $ moles $\times M_r = 2\,010\,000 \times 44.0 = 88\,440\,000$ g
88 440 000 g $= 88\,440\,000 \div 1\,000\,000$
$= $ **88.4 tonnes** *[1 mark]*

b) $M_r(NH_3) = 14.0 + (1.0 \times 3) = 17.0$
59.5 tonnes $= 59.5 \times 1\,000\,000 = 59\,500\,000$ g
moles $= $ mass $\div M_r$
$= 59\,500\,000 \div 17.0 = 3\,500\,000$ moles *[1 mark]*

From the reaction equation, 2 moles of NH_3 make 1 mole of $(NH_2)_2CO$, so 3 500 000 moles of NH_3 will make $(3\,500\,000 \div 2 =) 1\,750\,000$ moles of $(NH_2)_2CO$.
From a), $M_r((NH_2)_2CO) = 60.0$
mass $= $ moles $\times M_r = 1\,750\,000 \times 60.0 = 105\,000\,000$ g
105 000 000 $= 105\,000\,000 \div 1\,000\,000$
$= $ **105 tonnes** *[1 mark]*
difference between masses of $(NH_2)_2CO = 120.6 - 105$
$= $ **15.6 tonnes** *[1 mark]*

Pages 36-37 — More Mole Calculations

1 a) All the carbon in CO_2 (4 moles of C atoms) must have come from A, so must all the hydrogen in 4 moles of H_2O (8 moles of H atoms), so the formula of the hydrocarbon must be C_4H_8 *[1 mark for correct number of Cs, 1 mark for correct number of Hs.]*.

b) $C_4H_8 + 6O_2 \rightarrow 4CO_2 + 4H_2O$ *[1 mark]*

2 a) $280 - 200 = $ **80 g** *[1 mark]*

b) moles $= $ mass $\div M_r$
moles of X $= 200 \div 40 = 5$ moles *[1 mark]*
moles of $O_2 = 80 \div (2 \times 16) = 2.5$ moles *[1 mark]*
There are twice as many moles of X as O_2, so the reaction must happen in a 2 : 1 ratio of X to O_2.
$2X + O_2 \rightarrow X$ oxide
Since all of the reactants end up in the products, and there are two atoms of X and O on the left-hand side of the equation, the formula of X oxide must be X_1O_1, or XO.
So, balanced equation $= 2X + O_2 \rightarrow 2XO$
[1 mark for correct left-hand side of the equation, 1 mark for correct right-hand side of the equation.]

3 a) i) H_2O *[1 mark]*
The products of neutralisation reactions are always a salt and water, so Y must be water.

ii) $H_2X + 2NaOH \rightarrow Na_2X + 2H_2O$
[1 mark for left-hand side correct, 1 mark for right-hand side correct]
X must have a charge of −2, since it's balanced by 2 hydrogen ions (which have a charge of +1 each). So, you must need 2 Na^+ ions to balance it, giving a formula of Na_2X.

b) i) $M_r(H_2O) = (1 \times 2) + 16 = 18$
mass of $H_2O = 228.2 - 156.2 = 72$ g *[1 mark]*
moles $= $ mass $\div M_r = 72 \div 18 = $ **4 moles** *[1 mark]*

ii) From the balanced equation, 2 moles of NaOH produced 2 moles of H_2O. So, if 4 moles of H_2O were produced, 4 moles of NaOH must have been used *[1 mark]*.
$M_r(NaOH) = 23 + 16 + 1 = 40$
mass $= $ moles $\times M_r = 4 \times 40 = $ **160 g** *[1 mark]*

iii) Since 160 g of the reactants were NaOH,
mass of acid $= 228.2 - 160 = 68.2$ g *[1 mark]*
From the equation, 2 moles of H_2O are produced by 1 mole of H_2X. So, 4 moles of H_2O (from part b) i)) would be produced by 2 moles of H_2X *[1 mark]*.
$M_r = $ mass $\div$ moles $= 68.2 \div 2 = $ **34.1** *[1 mark]*

iv) $M_r(H_2CrO_4) = 118$
$M_r(H_2S) = 34.1$
$M_r(H_2SO_4) = 98.1$. So, the acid is **H_2S** *[1 mark]*.

Page 38 — Endothermic and Exothermic Reactions

1 B *[1 mark]*

2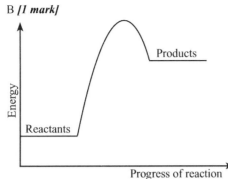

[1 mark for reactants and products correctly labelled and at appropriate energies, 1 mark for correct shape of curve]

3 a)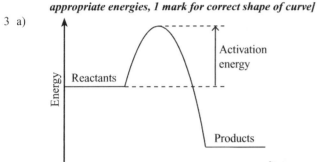

[1 mark]

b) An exothermic reaction because the reactants have more energy than the products / energy is released during the reaction *[1 mark]*.

Pages 39-40 — Bond Energies

1 C *[1 mark]*

2 a) energy change = energy required to break bonds –
               energy released by forming bonds
bonds broken: $1 \times C=C + 1 \times H$—$O$
    $= 614 + 463 = 1077$ kJ/mol *[1 mark]*
bonds made: $1 \times C$—$C + 1 \times C$—$H + 1 \times C$—O
    $= 347 + 413 + 358 = 1118$ kJ/mol *[1 mark]*
energy change = $1077 - 1118 = $ **–41 kJ/mol** *[1 mark]*

If there are any bonds that appear on both sides of the equation, you can ignore them when you work out the energies of the bonds broken and the bonds made — that's what we've done here. But if you find it easier to work out the total energy of all the bonds in the products and the total energy of all the bonds in the reactants, you'll still get the same answer.

b) The reaction is exothermic *[1 mark]* as the energy change of reaction is negative / energy is given out during the reaction / it takes less energy to break the bonds in the reactants than the energy given out when the bonds in the products are made *[1 mark]*.

3 a) exothermic *[1 mark]*

b) energy change = energy required to break bonds –
               energy released by forming bonds
bonds broken: $1 \times C$—$H + 1 \times Cl$—Cl
    $= 413 + 239 = 652$ kJ/mol
bonds made: $1 \times C$—$Cl + 1 \times H$—$Cl = 339 + H$—Cl
$-119 = 652 - (339 + H$—$Cl)$
$-119 = 313 - H$—Cl
H—$Cl = 313 + 119 = $ **432 kJ/mol**

[3 marks for the correct answer, otherwise 1 mark for correct expression for the value of the H—Cl bond in terms of the energy change of reaction and the energies of the bonds made and broken, 1 mark for correctly calculating energies of bonds made and broken]

c) Cl—Cl, C—Cl, C—C, C—H, H—Cl
[1 mark for correct order, using value for H—Cl calculated in part b).]

Stronger bonds take more energy to break, so stronger bonds will have higher bond energies.

Pages 41-42 — Acids and Bases

Warm-up
The following sentences should be circled:
As H^+ concentration increases, pH decreases.
Alkalis turn Universal indicator blue/purple.
Acids have pHs of less than 7.
Alkalis are soluble bases.

1 A *[1 mark]*

2 a) red/orange *[1 mark]*

b) Any answer between 8 and 14 *[1 mark]*

c) pH probe / pH meter *[1 mark]*

3 $H^+_{(aq)} + OH^-_{(aq)} \rightarrow H_2O_{(l)}$ *[1 mark for correct equation, 1 mark for correct state symbols.]*

4 C *[1 mark]*

5 a) 1 *[1 mark]*

b)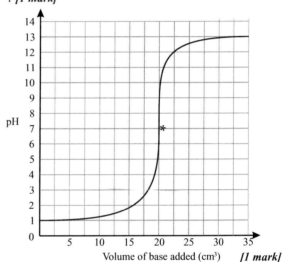

[1 mark]

c) 20 cm³ *[1 mark]*

d) At the end point, the concentration of hydrogen ions is equal / the same as the concentration of hydroxide ions *[1 mark]*.

Page 43 — Strong and Weak Acids

1 a) A weak acid doesn't fully ionise in solution / only a small proportion of molecules in a weak acid dissociate to release hydrogen ions *[1 mark]*.

b) $HCOOH \rightleftharpoons HCOO^- + H^+$ *[1 mark for correct equation, 1 mark for arrow showing reversible reaction.]*

2 A *[1 mark]*

3 a) D *[1 mark]*

b) 1 *[1 mark]*

An increase in the hydrogen ion concentration by a factor of 10 decreases the pH by 1. So an increase by a factor of 100 will reduce the pH by 2.

Pages 44-45 — Reactions of Acids

1 D *[1 mark]*

2 From top to bottom:
$Zn(NO_3)_2$ *[1 mark]*, $CaSO_4$ *[1 mark]*,
Na_2SO_4 *[1 mark]*, KCl *[1 mark]*

3 a) It dissolves in water *[1 mark]*.

b) $2KOH + H_2SO_4 \rightarrow K_2SO_4 + 2H_2O$
[2 marks for all formulas correct and a correctly-balanced equation, otherwise 1 mark for correct formulas in an unbalanced equation.]

c) No, the salt will be contaminated by the indicator *[1 mark]*.

4 a)   carbon dioxide *[1 mark]*

b) $ZnCO_3 + 2HCl \rightarrow ZnCl_2 + H_2O + CO_2$
[2 marks for all formulas correct and a correctly-balanced equation, otherwise 1 mark for correct formulas in an unbalanced equation.]

c)   zinc chloride *[1 mark]*

5 a) $H_2SO_4 + 2NaOH \rightarrow Na_2SO_4 + 2H_2O$
[2 marks for all formulas correct and a correctly-balanced equation, otherwise 1 mark for correct formulas in an unbalanced equation.]

b)   How to grade your answer:

Level 0:   There is no relevant information. *[No marks]*

Level 1:   There is a brief explanation of how to prepare the salt but no details are given. *[1 to 2 marks]*

Level 2:   There is some explanation of to prepare the salt, including necessary equipment and how to isolate the salt, but the method is missing key details. *[3 to 4 marks]*

Level 3:   There is a clear and detailed explanation of to produce and extract a pure sample of the salt. *[5 to 6 marks]*

Here are some points your answer may include:
Place a known volume of sulfuric acid and an indicator in a conical flask.
Slowly add sodium hydroxide with a burette until the indicator changes colour (this is the end point).
Repeat the experiment using the same volumes of acid and alkali, but with no indicator.
Slowly evaporate off some of the water and leave the salt to crystallise.
Filter out the solid and dry it (e.g. in a drying oven or using a desiccator).

Pages 46-47 — Making Salts

1   D *[1 mark]*

2 a)   E.g. hydrochloric acid *[1 mark]*

b)   Jeremy has poured too much solution into the funnel / the level of the solution goes above the filter paper *[1 mark]*. This means that some of the solid can pass down the sides of the filter paper and into the conical flask below, reducing the amount of solid that's extracted from the solution *[1 mark]*.

c)   Deionised water doesn't contain any other ions which might otherwise contaminate the pure salt *[1 mark]*.

3 a)   C *[1 mark]*

b) $Mg(OH)_{2\,(s)} + H_2SO_{4\,(aq)} \rightarrow MgSO_{4\,(aq)} + 2H_2O_{(l)}$
[2 marks for all formulas correct and a correctly-balanced equation, otherwise 1 mark for correct formulas in an unbalanced equation.]

4 a) $Fe(OH)_3$ *[1 mark]*

b)   E.g. she should wait for the reaction to reach completion before filtering out the precipitate *[1 mark]*. She should dry the solid in a desiccator/in the air, and not using a Bunsen burner *[1 mark]*.

Page 48 — Oxidation and Reduction

1   Oxidation can describe the addition of oxygen. During the combustion of a hydrocarbon, the hydrocarbon is burnt in oxygen so oxygen-containing products are made *[1 mark]*.

2   C *[1 mark]*

3 a) $Al \rightarrow Al^{3+} + 3e^-$ *[1 mark]*

b)   reducing agent *[1 mark]*

4 a) i) $Zn \rightarrow Zn^{2+} + 2e^-$ *[1 mark]*

ii) $2H^+ + 2e^- \rightarrow H_2$ *[1 mark]*

b)   hydrogen ions / H^+ ions *[1 mark]*

c)   zinc *[1 mark]*

Pages 49-50 — Electrolysis

Warm-up

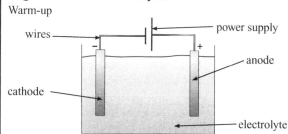

1 a)   The ions in solid sodium chloride are not free to move and so can't carry a charge *[1 mark]*, when sodium chloride is molten or dissolved it can carry a charge as the ions are free to move around *[1 mark]*.

b) i)   chlorine (gas) *[1 mark]*

ii)   sodium (metal) *[1 mark]*

2 a) PbI_2 *[1 mark]*

b)   Lead metal would form at the cathode *[1 mark]*.

3   E.g. there is no power supply *[1 mark]*. The electrodes are not submerged in the electrolyte *[1 mark]*.

4 a)   Disagree. Potassium nitrate solution will contain hydrogen and hydroxide ions, as well as potassium and nitrate ions *[1 mark]*. Since potassium is more reactive than hydrogen, hydrogen will be discharged instead *[1 mark]*.

b)   At the anode, you would see bubbles of gas *[1 mark]* as oxygen is evolved *[1 mark]*.

5 a)   B *[1 mark]*

b) i)   A green vapour would form *[1 mark]*.

ii)   Copper metal would coat the electrode *[1 mark]*.

Pages 51-52 — Electrolysis of Copper Sulfate

1 a)   Inert electrodes do not react with the electrolyte *[1 mark]*.

b) $H^+, SO_4^{2-}, Cu^{2+}, OH^-$ *[2 marks for all four correct, otherwise 1 mark for any 3 correct.]*

c) i) $4OH^- \rightarrow O_2 + 2H_2O + 4e^-$ *[1 mark]*

ii) $Cu^{2+} + 2e^- \rightarrow Cu$ *[1 mark]*

2 a)   The mass of the cell would not change *[1 mark]*.

b)   The mass/size of the cathode would have increased, but the mass/size of the anode would have decreased *[1 mark]*. This is because, during the electrolysis, the electrical current pulls electrons off Cu atoms at the anode, causing them to move into solution as Cu^{2+} ions and causing the mass of the anode to decrease *[1 mark]*. They regain electrons at the cathode to become Cu atoms again, which plate the cathode, causing its mass to increase *[1 mark]*.

3   D *[1 mark]*

4   The mass of cell A would be less than the mass of cell B after 5 hours *[1 mark]*. In cell A, copper metal plates the cathode: $Cu^{2+} + 2e^- \rightarrow Cu$ *[1 mark]*. But at the anode, oxygen gas is formed: $4OH^- \rightarrow O_2 + 2H_2O + 4e^-$. This means mass is lost from the cell as oxygen gas escapes from the system, so the mass would decrease *[1 mark]*. In cell B, as with cell A, copper metal plates the cathode: $Cu^{2+} + 2e^- \rightarrow Cu$ *[1 mark]*. But at the anode, copper is oxidised to copper ions: $Cu \rightarrow Cu^{2+} + 2e^-$, which remain in the system. Therefore the mass of cell B stays constant *[1 mark]*.

Topic C4 — Predicting and Identifying Reactions and Products

Page 53 — Group 1 — Alkali Metals

1 a)   The Group 1 elements all have one outer electron *[1 mark]*, so losing one electron gives them a 1+ charge with a stable electronic structure/full outer shell *[1 mark]*.

b)   Any answer in the range 80 °C to 140 °C *[1 mark]*.
The range of acceptable answers is quite big here, so you should get the mark as long as you use any sensible method to estimate the melting point.

2 a)   Sodium hydroxide *[1 mark]* and hydrogen *[1 mark]*.
b)   The potassium would float around on the surface of the water *[1 mark]*, fizzing vigorously *[1 mark]*. It would melt *[1 mark]* and ignite the hydrogen gas produced by the reaction *[1 mark]*.
c)   Rubidium is more reactive than potassium, so it will react violently with water / may explode when placed in water *[1 mark]*.

Pages 54-55 — Group 7 — Halogens

Warm-up

The five known Group 7 elements, or halogens, are fluorine, chlorine, bromine, **iodine** and astatine. They have similar chemical properties, because they all have **seven** electrons in their outer shell. The halogens exist as **diatomic** molecules, where two halogen atoms share a pair of electrons in a **covalent** bond. A halogen atom can also form a stable ion by gaining one electron — these ions are called **halide** ions.

1 a)   fluorine *[1 mark]*
If the boiling points of the elements increase as you go down a group, the one with the lowest boiling point must be at the top of the group.
b)   solid *[1 mark]*
Since the melting points of the elements increase down Group 7, if the element above astatine is solid at room temperature and pressure, astatine should be solid too.

2 a) i)   sodium bromide *[1 mark]*
   ii) potassium iodide *[1 mark]*
b) $2Li + Cl_2 \rightarrow 2LiCl$
        [1 mark for all reactants and products correct,
        1 mark for equation being correctly balanced.]

3 a)   no reaction *[1 mark]*
b)   Iodine is less reactive than bromine *[1 mark]*, so iodine cannot displace bromine from sodium bromide *[1 mark]*.
c) $Cl_2 + 2NaBr \rightarrow Br_2 + 2NaCl$
        [1 mark for all reactants and products correct,
        1 mark for equation being correctly balanced.]

4 a)   Reactivity decreases as you go down Group 7 *[1 mark]*.
b)   Halogen atoms only need to gain one electron to form a 1⁻ ion with a stable electronic structure/full outer shell *[1 mark]*. The easier it is for a halogen atom to attract an electron, the more reactive it will be *[1 mark]*. As you go down Group 7, it gets harder for the halogen atoms to attract an electron, since the outer shell is further away from the nucleus/the atomic radius is larger *[1 mark]*.

Page 56 — Group 0 — Noble Gases

1   C *[1 mark]*
2 a)   The noble gases all have a full outer shell of electrons, giving them a stable electronic structure *[1 mark]*. This means that they won't easily either give up or gain electrons, making them inert *[1 mark]*.
b) i)   Any answer in the range 4.1 kg/m³ to 7.0 kg/m³ *[1 mark]*
   ii) Higher, because the melting points of the elements increase as you go down Group 0 *[1 mark]*.

Pages 57-58 — Transition Metals

Warm-up

The transition metals can be found **in the middle** of the periodic table. The elements that should be circled are: nickel, chromium, silver, titanium and cobalt.

1 a)   E.g. transition metals conduct electricity well
        [1 mark for any correct property related to the given use].
b)   E.g. transition metals have high melting points
        [1 mark for any correct property related to the given use].

c)   E.g. transition metals have colourful compounds
        [1 mark for any correct property related to the given use].
d)   E.g. transition metals are unreactive/resistant to corrosion
        [1 mark for any correct property related to the given use].
If you didn't give the properties shown here, you still get a mark for any property of a transition metal that's clearly connected to the use. For example if you wrote 'malleable' for d, you'd get the mark, because you do need to be able to shape a material easily if you're making it into pipes.

2 a)   They can form more than one ion / form ions with different charges *[1 mark]*.
b)   Vanadium acts as a catalyst *[1 mark]*.
c)   You would expect the deep blue powder to be vanadium(IV) oxide, because transition metal compounds are usually colourful *[1 mark]*.

3 a)   Metal B is more likely to be a transition metal, because transition metals usually have high melting points *[1 mark]*.
b)   Metal D is more likely to be a transition metal. When it was placed in the water, it sank/didn't float *[1 mark]* and it didn't react/fizz/produce bubbles of hydrogen gas *[1 mark]*.
Most transition metals have high densities and are relatively unreactive, so you'd expect them to sink and not to react when you put them in water.

Pages 59-60 — Reactivity of Metals

1 a)   Most reactive: magnesium
                          zinc
                          iron
        Least reactive: copper
        [1 mark for putting magnesium at the top and copper at the bottom. 1 mark for putting zinc above iron in the middle.]
b) i)   zinc oxide *[1 mark]*
   ii) Metal X was sodium, because it reacted vigorously with cold water *[1 mark]*.
2   A *[1 mark]*
3 a)   Yes, because lead can displace silver from a salt solution / silver cannot displace lead from a salt solution *[1 mark]*.
b) $3Mg + 2AlCl_3 \rightarrow 2Al + 3MgCl_2$
        [2 marks for all formulas correct and a correctly-balanced equation, otherwise 1 mark for correct formulas in an unbalanced equation]
c)   The solution would change colour from colourless to green *[1 mark]*. The piece of shiny grey nickel will be coated in dull grey lead *[1 mark]*.

Page 61 — Tests for Gases

1 a)   damp blue litmus paper *[1 mark]*
b)   chlorine *[1 mark]*
2 a)   E.g. the gas could be toxic/an irritant *[1 mark]*
b)   Bubble the gas through limewater *[1 mark]*. If the gas is carbon dioxide, the limewater will turn cloudy *[1 mark]*.
c)   The gas was not hydrogen *[1 mark]*
d)   oxygen *[1 mark]*

Pages 62-64 — Tests for Ions

1 a) i)   E.g. hydrochloric acid *[1 mark]*
   ii) brick red *[1 mark]*
b) i)   barium sulfate *[1 mark]*
   ii) Nothing will happen *[1 mark]*, because barium sulfate does not react with hydrochloric acid *[1 mark]*.
2 a)   lithium / Li⁺ *[1 mark]*
b) i)   blue-green *[1 mark]*
   ii) A blue precipitate would form *[1 mark]*.
3 a) Fe^{3+} / iron(III) *[1 mark]*
b) FeI_2 *[1 mark]*
The green precipitate with sodium hydroxide tells you that it contains Fe^{2+} ions. The yellow precipitate with silver nitrate tells you that it contains I⁻ ions. The formula of the compound must be FeI_2 to balance the charges.

Topic C5

c) i) No, because other metal ions (e.g. calcium) can also react with sodium hydroxide to form a white precipitate *[1 mark]*.

ii) The white precipitate would dissolve, leaving a colourless solution *[1 mark]*.

4 a) The compound contains both sodium and potassium ions, so a flame test would give a mixture of colours *[1 mark]*.

b) Add barium chloride solution *[1 mark]*. A white precipitate will form *[1 mark]*. Now add dilute hydrochloric acid *[1 mark]*. The precipitate will react with the acid and the mixture will fizz/bubble *[1 mark]*. If you collect the gas produced and pass it through limewater, the limewater should turn cloudy *[1 mark]*.

5 How to grade your answer:

Level 0: There is no relevant information. *[No marks]*

Level 1: There is a brief explanation of how to test the compound for either potassium ions or chloride ions. *[1 to 2 marks]*

Level 2: There is some explanation of how to test the compound for both potassium ions and chloride ions. *[3 to 4 marks]*

Level 3: There is a clear and detailed explanation of how to test the compound for both potassium ions and chloride ions. *[5 to 6 marks]*

Here are some points your answer may include:

To test the compound for potassium ions:

Oliver could carry out a flame test to show whether or not the compound contains potassium ions.

To do this, he should clean a wire loop by dipping it into hydrochloric acid and rinsing it in distilled water.

Then he should dip the wire loop into his compound and put the loop in the clear blue part of a Bunsen flame.

If the compound contains potassium ions, Oliver should see a lilac flame.

To test the compound for chloride ions:

To test for chloride ions, Oliver will first need to dissolve a little of the solid salt in distilled water.

Next he should add a little dilute nitric acid.

Then he should add a few drops of silver nitrate solution.

If the compound contains chloride ions, a white precipitate should form.

Pages 65-66 — Chemical Analysis

1 E.g. instrumental methods are very sensitive / can detect very small amounts of a substance *[1 mark]*. Instrumental methods are very fast *[1 mark]*. Instrumental methods are very accurate *[1 mark]*.

2 a) four *[1 mark]*

b) propene and butanol *[1 mark each for propene and butanol. Lose 1 mark if you also listed a third incorrect substance. 0 marks for listing all four substances.]*

3 a) Peak A: C–C
Peak B: C–O
Peak C: C–H
Peak D: O–H (in an alcohol)
[2 marks for all four correct, 1 mark for two or three correct, 0 marks for none or one correct.]

b) Any two from: e.g. propene contains a C=C bond, but there is no peak at the frequency for a C=C bond on the spectrum. / There is a peak at the frequency for a C–O bond on the spectrum, but there is no C–O bond in propene. / There is a peak at the frequency for an O–H bond on the spectrum, but there is no O–H bond in propene *[1 mark for each correct reason]*.

Topic C5 — Monitoring and Controlling Chemical Reactions

Pages 67-68 — Concentration

Warm-up

1 A *[1 mark]*

2 a) $220 \text{ cm}^3 = (220 \div 1000) \text{ dm}^3 = 0.220 \text{ dm}^3$
Mass = concentration × volume = $75.0 × 0.220 = \textbf{16.5 g}$
[1 mark]

b) $75.0 \div 159.6 = \textbf{0.47 mol/dm}^3$ *[1 mark]*

c) B *[1 mark]*

3 a) $400 \text{ cm}^3 = (400 \div 1000) \text{ dm}^3 = 0.4 \text{ dm}^3$
Concentration = mass ÷ volume = $56 \div 0.4$
$= \textbf{140 g/dm}^3$ *[1 mark]*

b) $300 \text{ cm}^3 = (300 \div 1000) \text{ dm}^3 = 0.300 \text{ dm}^3$
Mass = concentration × volume = $140 × 0.300 = \textbf{42 g}$ *[1 mark]*

If your answer to part a) was incorrect, award 1 mark for correct working in part b).

4 a) $600 \text{ cm}^3 = (600 \div 1000) \text{ dm}^3 = 0.6 \text{ dm}^3$
Number of moles = $5 × 0.6 = 3 \text{ mol}$
Mass = mol × M_r = $3 × 40.0 = \textbf{120 g}$
[2 marks for correct answer, otherwise 1 mark for working out number of moles of NaOH]

b) i) Volume = mass ÷ concentration = $36.0 \div 80.0 = 0.450 \text{ dm}^3$
$0.45 \text{ dm}^3 = (0.45 × 1000) \text{ cm}^3 = \textbf{450 cm}^3$
[2 marks for correct answer, otherwise 1 mark for calculating volume in dm³]

ii) Double the volume of water / add an extra 450 cm³ of water to the solution *[1 mark]*.

Pages 69-70 — Titrations

1 a) Mean titre = $(33.30 + 33.40 + 33.35) \div 3 = \textbf{33.35 cm}^3$
[1 mark]

b) Number of moles = $(33.35 \div 1000) × 0.165$
$= \textbf{0.00550 mol}$ *[1 mark]*

Even if your answer to part a) was incorrect, you'd get a mark for b) if you used carried out the calculation correctly.

2 a) Moles = concentration × volume
Moles of NaOH = $0.100 × (40.0 \div 1000) = 0.00400 \text{ mol}$
1 mole of NaOH reacts with 1 mole of HCl.
So, 0.00400 mol NaOH reacts with 0.00400 mol HCl.
Concentration of HCl = $0.00400 \div (20 \div 1000)$
$= \textbf{0.200 mol/dm}^3$
[2 marks for correct answer, otherwise 1 mark for correct moles of HCl]

b) M_r(HCl) = $35.5 + 1 = 36.5$
Concentration (g/dm³) = concentration (mol/dm³) × M_r
Concentration = $0.200 × 36.5 = \textbf{7.30 g/dm}^3$ *[2 marks for correct answer, otherwise 1 mark for correct M_r of HCl]*

If you got the wrong answer in part a) but carried out the correct calculations in part b), you'd still get the mark.

3 B *[1 mark]*

*2 moles of KOH reacts with 1 mole of H_2SO_4.
So, 0.00850 mol KOH reacts with 0.00425 mol H_2SO_4.
Concentration = moles ÷ volume
Concentration of H_2SO_4 = $0.00425 \div 0.0250 = 0.170 \text{ mol/dm}^3$
Concentration (g/dm³) = concentration (mol/dm³) × M_r
$= 0.170 × 98.1 = \textbf{16.7 g/dm}^3$*

Topic C5

4 a) How to grade your answer:

Level 0: There is no relevant information. *[No marks]*

Level 1: There is a brief explanation of how to carry a titration but it is not detailed and little technical equipment is mentioned. *[1 to 2 marks]*

Level 2: There is an explanation of how to carry out a titration and some of the equipment required, but there are limited details. *[3 to 4 marks]*

Level 3: There is a clear and detailed explanation of how to carry out a titration and all the equipment needed is clearly included. *[5 to 6 marks]*

Here are some points your answer may include:
Measure out a known volume of the sodium hydroxide solution using a pipette and put it in a conical flask.
Add a few drops of an indicator to the sodium hydroxide.
Use the burette to add the sulfuric acid to the sodium hydroxide, swirling the conical flask regularly.
Stop the titration when the indicator changes colour, this is when the sodium hydroxide is completely neutralised.
Record the volume of sulfuric acid required to cause this colour change.
Repeat the titration with the same volume of sodium hydroxide solution, but add the acid one drop at a time, close to the end point.
Record the exact volume of sulfuric acid required to neutralise the sodium hydroxide.
Repeat the titration several times until there are at least three concordant titres.
Calculate a mean titre from the concordant titres, ignoring any anomalous results.

b) Moles = concentration × volume
Moles of H_2SO_4 = $0.200 \times (22.5 \div 1000) = 0.00450$ moles
1 mole of H_2SO_4 reacts with 2 moles of NaOH.
So, 0.00450 moles of H_2SO_4 reacts with (0.00450×2)
= 0.00900 moles of NaOH
Concentration of NaOH = $0.00900 \div (25.0 \div 1000)$
= **0.360 mol/dm³**
[2 marks for correct answer, otherwise 1 mark for correct moles of NaOH]

Page 71 — Calculations with Gases

1 a) Chloé is correct. At RTP, one mole of any gas occupies 24 dm³ *[1 mark]*. So, 23.0 moles of carbon dioxide and 23.0 moles of oxygen will occupy the same volume *[1 mark]*.

b) 1 mole = 24.0 dm³
23.0 moles = 23.0×24.0 = **552 dm³** *[1 mark]*

2 a) $M_r(CO_2) = 12 + 16 + 16 = 44$
Moles = mass ÷ M_r = $1.76 \div 44 = 0.040$ mol
920 cm³ = $(920 \div 1000)$ dm³ = 0.92 dm³
Molar volume = volume ÷ moles = $0.92 \div 0.040$
= **23 dm³/mol** *[2 marks for correct answer, otherwise 1 mark for correct moles of CO_2]*

b) 175 cm³ = $(175 \div 1000)$ dm³ = 0.175 dm³
Moles = volume ÷ molar volume = $0.175 \div 25.0$
= 0.00700 mol
$M_r(CO_2) = 12.0 + 16.0 + 16.0 = 44.0$
Mass = $M_r \times$ moles = 44.0×0.007 = **0.31 g** *[2 marks for correct answer, otherwise 1 mark correct moles of CO_2]*

Pages 72-73 — Percentage Yield

1 a) C *[1 mark]*

b) Percentage yield = $(22 \div 25) \times 100$ = **88%** *[1 mark]*

2 a) $M_r(CuSO_4) = 63.5 + 32.1 + (4 \times 16.0) = 159.6$
$M_r(Cu(OH)_2) = 63.5 + [2 \times (16.0 + 1.0)] = 97.5$
Moles = mass ÷ $M_r(CuSO_4) = 39.75 \div 159.6 = 0.2491$ mol
1 mole of $CuSO_4$ produces 1 mole of $Cu(OH)_2$.

So, 0.2491 moles of $CuSO_4$ should produce 0.2491 moles of $Cu(OH)_2$.
Theoretical yield = 0.2491×97.5 = **24.3 g**
[3 marks for correct answer, otherwise 1 mark for correct moles of $CuSO_4$ and 1 mark for correct moles of $Cu(OH)_2$]

b) Percentage yield = $(16.5 \div 24.3) \times 100$ = **67.9%** *[1 mark]*
If your answer to part a) was incorrect, award 1 mark for correct working in part b).

3 a) $M_r(CaCO_3) = 40.1 + 12.0 + (3 \times 16.0) = 100.1$
$M_r(CaO) = 40.1 + 16.0 = 56.1$
Moles = mass ÷ M_r
Moles $(CaCO_3) = (68.00 \times 1000) \div 100.1 = 679.3...$ mol
1 mole of $CaCO_3$ produces 1 mole of CaO. So, 679.3... moles of $CaCO_3$ should produce 679 moles of CaO.
Theoretical yield = $679.3... \times 56.1 = 38\,109...$ g = 38.10... kg
Percentage yield = $(28.56 \div 38.09) \times 100$ = **74.9%**
[4 marks for correct answer, otherwise 1 mark for correct moles of $CaCO_3$, 1 mark for correct moles of CaO and 1 mark for calculating the theoretical yield of CaO]

b) $M_r(CaO) = 40.1 + 16.0 = 56.1$
$M_r(Ca(OH)_2) = 40.1 + [2 \times (16.0 + 1.0)] = 74.1$
Moles = mass ÷ $M_r = (28.56 \times 1000) \div 56.1 = 509.0...$ moles
1 mole of CaO produces 1 mole of $Ca(OH)_2$.
So, 509.0... moles of CaO should produce 509.0... moles of $Ca(OH)_2$.
Theoretical yield = $509.0... \times 74.1 = 37\,723$ g = 37.72... kg
Percentage yield = $(32.80 \div 37.72) \times 100$ = **87.0%**
[4 marks for correct answer, otherwise 1 mark for correct moles of CaO, 1 mark for correct moles of $Ca(OH)_2$, and 1 mark for calculating the theoretical yield of $Ca(OH)_2$]

c) The reaction producing the calcium hydroxide is more economic as it has the greatest percentage yield *[1 mark]* which means that less reactants have been wasted which reduces cost *[1 mark]*.

Pages 74-75 — Atom Economy

Warm-up

Reaction	Atom economy (%)
NaOH + HCl → NaCl + H_2O	76.5
$2Cu + O_2 \rightarrow 2CuO$	100

1 a) i) The percentage of reactants turned into useful products *[1 mark]*.

ii) Atom economy = $(111 \div 141) \times 100$ = **78.7%** *[1 mark]*

b) Reaction A. It has 100% atom economy so all of the reactants are turned into a useful product *[1 mark]*. It also has the highest percentage yield, so there should be the least waste produced *[1 mark]*. It has the second highest rate of reaction, so it produces the required amount of product in a sensible length of time *[1 mark]*.

2 a) M_r of desired product = $M_r(MgCl_2) = [24.3 + (2 \times 35.5)] = 95.3$
Reaction X:
M_r of all products = $M_r(MgCl_2) + M_r(H_2)$
= $95.3 + (2 \times 1.0) = 95.3 + 2.0 = 97.3$
Atom economy = $(95.3 \div 97.3) \times 100$ = **98%**
Reaction Y:
M_r of all products = $M_r(MgCl_2) + M_r(H_2O) + M_r(CO_2)$
= $95.3 + [(2 \times 1.0) + 16.0] + [12.0 + (2 \times 16.0)]$
= $95.3 + 18.0 + 44.0 = 157.3$
Atom economy = $(95.3 \div 157.3) \times 100$ = **61%**
Reaction Z:
M_r of all products = $M_r(MgCl_2) + M_r(H_2O)$
= $95.3 + [(2 \times 1.0) + 16.0]$
= $95.3 + 18.0 = 113.3$
Atom economy = $(95.3 \div 113.3) \times 100$ = **84%**

[7 marks for three correct answers, otherwise 1 mark for correct M_r of desired product ($MgCl_2$), 1 mark for correct M_r of all products in reaction X, 1 mark for correct atom economy of reaction X, 1 mark for correct M_r of all products in reaction Y, 1 mark for correct atom economy of reaction Y, 1 mark for correct M_r of all products in reaction Z and 1 mark for correct atom economy of reaction Z]

b) i) Reactions with low atom economies use more resources to produce a certain amount of product as less reactants are converted to useful products, so resources are used up quickly *[1 mark]*.

ii) Reactions with low atom economies produce more waste materials as more reactants are converted into by-products, and their disposal/removal can be expensive *[1 mark]*.

c) reaction Y *[1 mark]*

Pages 76-78 — Reaction Rates

1 a) Add the calcium carbonate to sulfuric acid in a conical flask and seal with a gas syringe *[1 mark]*. Immediately start the stopwatch and use the gas syringe to measure the volume of carbon dioxide produced *[1 mark]* at set time intervals until gas production stops *[1 mark]*. / Add the calcium carbonate to sulfuric acid in a conical flask and measure the mass of the flask and its contents *[1 mark]*. Immediately start the stopwatch and measure the loss in mass *[1 mark]* at set time intervals until the mass stops decreasing *[1 mark]*.

b) E.g.

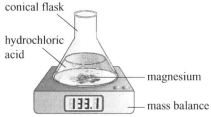

[1 mark]

The curve must have a steeper gradient and finish the reaction sooner than the original curve, but still produce the same maximum volume of CO_2

c) B *[1 mark]*

2 a) E.g.

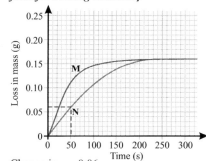

[1 mark for use of mass balance, 1 mark for use of conical flask for holding reactants]

b)

Change in $y = 0.06$
Change in $x = 50$
Gradient = change in $y \div$ change in x
$= 0.06 \div 50 = \textbf{0.0012 g/s}$
[2 marks for correct answer, otherwise 1 mark for a correct equation to calculate the gradient]

c) A: Relative rate (1/s) = $1 \div 243 = \textbf{0.00412}$
B: Relative rate (1/s) = $1 \div 371 = \textbf{0.00270}$
C: Relative rate (1/s) = $1 \div 286 = \textbf{0.00350}$
D: Relative rate (1/s) = $1 \div 435 = \textbf{0.00230}$
[2 marks for all four correct answers, otherwise 1 mark for any two correct answers]

d) D, B, C, A *[1 mark]*

3 a) i)

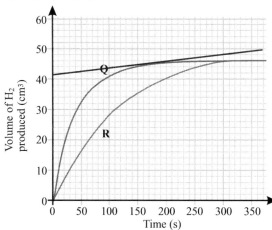

Change in $y = 48 - 42 = 6$
Change in $x = 300 - 30 = 270$
Gradient = change in $y \div$ change in $x = 6 \div 270$
$= \textbf{0.022 cm}^3\textbf{/s}$
Accept answers between 0.0100 cm^3/s and 0.0400 cm^3/s.
[2 marks for correct answer, otherwise 1 mark for drawing a correct tangent]

ii)

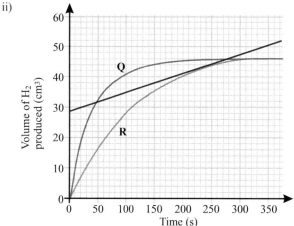

Change in $y = 48 - 36 = 12$
Change in $x = 310 - 120 = 190$
Gradient = change in $y \div$ change in $x = 12 \div 190$
$= \textbf{0.063 cm}^3\textbf{/s}$
Accept answers between 0.050 cm^3/s and 0.075 cm^3/s.
[2 marks for correct answer, otherwise 1 mark for drawing a correct tangent]

b) Reaction Q, as the reaction using powdered zinc would be faster *[1 mark]*. The steeper gradient of the graph for reaction Q shows that it was faster than R *[1 mark]*.

Page 79 — Collision Theory

1 a) Increase the pressure *[1 mark]*.

b) Increasing the pressure means that the particles are more crowded / there are more particles in a given volume *[1 mark]*. This means that the frequency of successful collisions between particles will increase and so the rate will increase *[1 mark]*.

2 a) Horatio is incorrect. Increasing the temperature to 45 °C will cause the particles to move faster which results in more frequent collisions *[1 mark]*. Higher temperatures also increase the energy of collisions which means more collisions will be successful *[1 mark]*. So, the reaction will have a higher rate at the higher temperature *[1 mark]*.

b) i) A *[1 mark]*

ii) It has the lowest concentration *[1 mark]* so there are less particles of hydrochloric acid in the same volume, so collisions are less likely *[1 mark]*.

Page 80 — Catalysts

1 C *[1 mark]*

2 a) She should compare the mass and appearance of the powder before and after the reaction *[1 mark]*. If the manganese(IV) oxide is a catalyst, the mass and appearance of the powder should both remain unchanged *[1 mark]*.

b) The catalyst decreases the energy needed for the reaction to occur *[1 mark]* by providing an alternative reaction pathway that has a lower activation energy *[1 mark]*.

c) A: reactants *[1 mark]*
B: activation energy with a catalyst *[1 mark]*
C: activation energy without a catalyst *[1 mark]*
D: products *[1 mark]*

Pages 81-82 — Dynamic Equilibrium

Warm-up
In a reaction, as the concentration of the reactants falls, the rate of the forward reaction **decreases** and as the concentration of the products rises, the rate of the backward reaction **increases**. When both the forward and backward reaction are going at **the same rate**, they are at equilibrium. At this point, the concentration of the reactants and products will **not change**.

1 a) In a reversible reaction, the products can react with each other to produce the original reactants *[1 mark]*.

b) The concentration of the reactants should be increased *[1 mark]*.

2 a) The concentration of the products is greater than the concentration of the reactants *[1 mark]*.

b) D *[1 mark]*

3 a) B *[1 mark]*

b) Equilibrium is only reached if the reaction occurs in a closed system where the reactants and products cannot escape *[1 mark]*.

4 a)

Test Tube	Condition	Colour of solution
A	Control	Red
B	Addition of $[Fe(SCN)]^{2+}$	Yellow/orange
C	Hot water bath	Yellow/orange
D	Ice bath	Dark red

[1 mark for each correct answer]

b) The forward reaction is exothermic, so increasing the temperature will shift the equilibrium to the left to absorb the extra heat *[1 mark]*. There will be less product and more reactant produced, so the solution will be yellow with the colour of Fe^{3+} *[1 mark]*.

c) Russell. Increasing the pressure only affects equilibria involving gases *[1 mark]*.

Topic C6 — Global Challenges

Page 83 — Extracting Metals from their Ores

1 a) A metal ore is a rock which contains enough metal to make it worthwhile extracting the metal from it *[1 mark]*.

b) Tin can be extracted from its ore by reduction with carbon *[1 mark]*.

c) Any one from: copper / zinc *[1 mark]*.

2 a) $2Fe_2O_3 + 3C \rightarrow 4Fe + 3CO_2$ *[1 mark for correct equation, 1 mark for correct balancing]*

b) The impurity is zinc as zinc is lower than carbon in the reactivity series/less reactive than carbon *[1 mark]*, so the zinc oxide present in the iron ore would have been reduced by carbon, as well as the iron oxide, in the blast furnace *[1 mark]*.

Calcium is more reactive than carbon so the calcium in calcium oxide wouldn't be reduced to calcium metal in the blast furnace.

Page 84 — Extracting Metals with Electrolysis

1 a) Extraction of aluminium requires electrolysis because it is more reactive than carbon *[1 mark]*. The electricity required for electrolysis is expensive *[1 mark]*. Iron can be extracted by reduction with carbon *[1 mark]*. This is much cheaper and requires less energy, so aluminium is more expensive to extract than iron *[1 mark]*.

b) Wires need to conduct electricity well, and impure copper is a bad conductor of electricity *[1 mark]*. Copper can be purified using electrolysis *[1 mark]*.

2 a) Plants are grown in soil containing metal compounds *[1 mark]*. Plants can neither use nor dispose of the metals, so they accumulate in the leaves *[1 mark]*. The plants are harvested, dried and burned in a furnace *[1 mark]*. Metals can be extracted from metal compounds in the ash using electrolysis or displacement reactions *[1 mark]*.

b) Advantage: e.g. less damaging to the environment *[1 mark]*. Disadvantage: e.g. process is very slow *[1 mark]*.

Page 85 — Alloys

Warm-up
Copper and Zinc

1 a) An alloy is a mixture of a metal and at least one other element *[1 mark]*.

b) Any one from: e.g. steel is harder / stronger / more resistant to corrosion *[1 mark]*.

c) B *[1 mark]*

2 E.g. Solder is the most suitable choice as it doesn't have a definite melting point, so gradually solidifies as it cools *[1 mark]*. This makes it much easier to work with when joining components in a circuit board *[1 mark]*.

You would also get the marks if you said that solder would be a good choice as it has a relatively low melting point so could be melted and worked with, without deforming or melting the other metal components in the circuit.

Page 86 — Corrosion

1 a) Iron + Oxygen + Water → Hydrated iron(III) oxide *[1 mark for correct reactants, 1 mark for correct product]*

b) In order for iron to rust, both oxygen and water are needed *[1 mark]*. If the bike is kept inside, the chain is less likely rust as it is less likely to come into contact with water *[1 mark]*.

c) i) B *[1 mark]*

ii) A bike chain involves a moving part, so oil is the best choice as it keeps oxygen and water off the chain *[1 mark]*, but still allows the chain to run smoothly *[1 mark]*.

2 a) The manufacturer should use magnesium blocks as magnesium is more reactive than steel *[1 mark]*, therefore the magnesium would lose electrons/oxidise and corrode instead of the steel *[1 mark]*. Tin is less reactive than steel, so wouldn't prevent the steel hull corroding *[1 mark]*.

Topic C6

b)   No, the zinc layer acts as sacrificial protection as well as a barrier / the zinc is more reactive than iron so it will lose electrons/oxidise in preference to iron, even if it's scratched *[1 mark]*.

Page 87 — The Haber Process

1 a) $N_2 + 3H_2 \rightleftharpoons 2NH_3$
[1 mark for correct reactants/product, 1 mark for correct balancing, 1 mark for use of reversible reaction arrow]
  b)   E.g. in fertilisers *[1 mark]*
2 a) i) A *[1 mark]*
   ii) Disagree. The forward reaction is exothermic so increasing the temperature moves the equilibrium position towards the reactants *[1 mark]*. This reduces the yield of ammonia *[1 mark]*.
  b)   E.g. it will decrease the rate of reaction / it will reduce the yield of ammonia *[1 mark for each correct reason, up to a maximum of 2 marks]*.
  c) i) The catalyst increases the rate of reaction *[1 mark]*.
   ii) The catalyst has no effect on the yield *[1 mark]*.

Page 88 — Fertilisers

Warm-up
Hydrogen can be obtained from **hydrocarbons** and **nitrogen** is extracted from the air. These two substances are reacted together in the **Haber process** to produce ammonia. Ammonia and **nitric acid** are then reacted together to make the fertiliser, **ammonium nitrate**.

1 a)   Phosphoric acid and ammonia *[1 mark]*.
  b)   Nitric acid and potassium hydroxide *[1 mark]*.
2 a)   burette *[1 mark]*
  b)   The student should have noted exactly how much ammonia it took to neutralise the sulfuric acid *[1 mark]*, then repeated the titration with the same volume of acid and alkali but without adding indicator *[1 mark]*.
  c)   Any one from: e.g. it is not practical to use the titration method for large, industrial quantities / crystallisation is a slow process *[1 mark]*.

Page 89 — The Contact Process

1   Step 2 involves a reversible reaction *[1 mark]* so the conditions need to be controlled so as to make sure the yield isn't significantly reduced *[1 mark]*.
2 a)   D *[1 mark]*
  b) i) A lower temperature increases the yield of sulfur trioxide *[1 mark]*. The forward reaction is exothermic, so a low temperature pushes the position of equilibrium to the right to try and compensate for the drop in temperature *[1 mark]*.
   ii) A lower temperature slows the rate of reaction *[1 mark]*. The particles move more slowly and so collisions are less frequent *[1 mark]*. The particles also have less energy so a smaller proportion of collisions are successful *[1 mark]*.

Page 90 — Industrial Processes

1 a)   E.g. crude oil is non-renewable so it will eventually run out *[1 mark]*.
  b)   Using the crude oil substitute might make the industrial reaction not profitable as high temperatures and pressures are expensive to maintain *[1 mark]*.
2 a)   pH = 6 *[1 mark]*, temperature = 60 °C *[1 mark]*
  b)   Using a temperature of 10 °C is not sensible as the rate at this temperature is very low, so the reaction would take a long time *[1 mark]*.
  c)   Advantage: e.g. the rate of reaction would increase *[1 mark]*. Disadvantage: e.g. high pressures are expensive to maintain *[1 mark]*.

Pages 91-92 — Life Cycle Assessments

Warm-up
Recyclability of the product
Source of raw materials

1 a)   A life cycle assessment looks at each stage of the life of a product to work out the potential environmental impact at each stage *[1 mark]*.
  b)   Timber is the better choice. Timber comes from a renewable source and so is sustainable *[1 mark]* whereas polypropene comes from crude oil which is non-renewable and so is not sustainable *[1 mark]*. The energy cost to extract timber from trees is also much lower than to make polypropene, meaning that less energy, from e.g. crude oil, is used, making the process more sustainable *[1 mark]*.
  c)   Any two from: e.g. how much waste was produced by the process / how much pollution the manufacturing process makes / how long the chairs last / how much water the process uses *[1 mark for each correct answer]*.
2 a)   E.g. out of the four toys, toy A has the highest CO_2 emissions, the highest solvent use and uses the highest amount of non-renewable energy. Therefore, toy A will have the greatest impact on the environment, so is the worst choice. Toy B has the second lowest CO_2 emissions, uses the least solvent but uses the second highest amount of non-renewable energy, so on balance looks a better choice than toy A. Toy C has the second highest CO_2 emissions and solvent use, but the lowest consumption of non-renewable energy. On balance, this looks like a worse choice than toy B. Toy D has the lowest CO_2 emissions and solvent use, and the second lowest consumption of non-renewable energy, so on balance, toy D is the best choice.
[1 mark for each valid comparison between the data in the table, up to a total of 3 marks. 1 mark for choosing toy D and giving suitable justification.]
  b)   E.g. extracting iron uses a lot of energy *[1 mark]* and creates lots of pollution *[1 mark]*.
  c)   Any one from: e.g. landfill takes up limited space / generates pollution *[1 mark]*.
  d)   C *[1 mark]*

Page 93 — Recycling Materials

1 a)   Material B should be recycled. Only a small amount of energy is needed to recycle it whereas a lot of energy is needed to extract the raw materials and make the material from scratch *[1 mark]*. There is also a limited availability of the resource B so it could soon run out if it is not recycled *[1 mark]*.
  b)   Crude oil is a non-renewable resource so it is important to conserve it *[1 mark]*.
  c) i) The different materials in the carton will need to be separated before they can be recycled and this can be expensive *[1 mark]*.
   ii) D *[1 mark]*
   iii) Any one from: e.g. toilet paper / low-quality cardboard *[1 mark]*.

Pages 94-95 — Types of Materials and their Uses

1 a)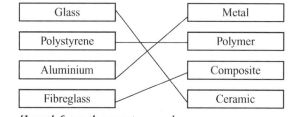
[1 mark for each correct answer]

Topic C6

b) Composite materials are made of one material embedded in another *[1 mark]*. The properties of a composite depend on the properties of the materials it is made from *[1 mark]*.

2 a) E.g. Plasticised PVC would be the best choice as it's an electrical insulator (it has low electrical conductivity) so will protect the surrounding environment from live electricity *[1 mark]*. It's the most flexible of the three materials which allows wires to bend to fit in and around different spaces *[1 mark]*. It's also cheap which keeps the cost down of electrical products containing lots of wiring *[1 mark]*.

b) Low-density polymers because they are light-weight and stretchy and can be squeezed *[1 mark]*. High-density polymers are rigid and so cannot be squeezed *[1 mark]*.

3 a) E.g. The hockey stick needs to be strong to withstand forces applied during the game. Carbon fibre and steel have the greatest strength (4100 MPa and 780 MPa, respectively). The stick needs to be lightweight. Carbon fibre has a much lower density than steel (1.5 g/cm³ compared to 7.8 g/cm³) so would be much lighter. Carbon fibre is also resistant to corrosion which is important if used in the rain. Though carbon fibre is expensive, because the hockey stick is a professional hockey stick, the cost of the stick can be high, so carbon fibre would be the best choice.
[1 mark for each valid comparison between properties from the table, up to a total of 3 marks. 1 mark for choosing a material and giving suitable justification of the choice.]

b) E.g. Bridges need to be strong and, from the choice, steel and carbon fibre are the strongest materials (780 MPa and 4100 MPa, respectively). Bridges are big structures so the cost of the material should be kept down and steel is much cheaper than carbon fibre. Steel is also not too heavy, so a steel bridge won't be too difficult to support *[1 mark]*. Bridges also need to be resistant to corrosion, and steel can be protected to prevent it corroding, so steel would be the best choice.
[1 mark for each valid comparison between properties from the table, up to a total of 3 marks. 1 mark for choosing a material and giving suitable justification of the choice.]

c) Pipes need to have a good resistance to corrosion, so PVC, carbon fibre and lead would be good choices. However PVC is a lot cheaper than lead and carbon fibre. PVC is also light-weight, which allows the pipes to be mounted on houses. The strength of the material is not an important factor, so the low strength of PVC is not an issue. Overall, PVC would be the best choice.
[1 mark for each valid comparison between properties from the table, up to a total of 3 marks. 1 mark for choosing a material and giving suitable justification of the choice.]

Pages 96-97 — Alkanes and Alkenes

1 a) i) ethane *[1 mark]*
   ii) 6 *[1 mark]*
b)

[1 mark]

2 a) C_nH_{2n} *[1 mark]*
b) C *[1 mark]*
c) Alkenes must contain at least two carbon atoms so that a double bond can form between them *[1 mark]*.

3 a) Burning the alkane in a limited supply of oxygen *[1 mark]*.
b) $C_3H_8 + 3\frac{1}{2}O_2 \rightarrow 3CO + 4H_2O$ *[1 mark for correct left-hand side, 1 mark for correct right-hand side]*

4 a)

[1 mark]

b) The solution would have turned from orange to colourless *[1 mark]*.
c) A *[1 mark]*
d) butane *[1 mark]*

Pages 98-99 — Alcohols

Warm-up
-OH

1 a) propanol *[1 mark]*
b) C_2H_5OH *[1 mark]*
c)

[1 mark]

2 a) -COOH *[1 mark]*
b) C_2H_5COOH *[1 mark]*
c) ethanoic acid *[1 mark]*

3 A *[1 mark]*

4 a) potassium manganate(VII) *[1 mark]*
b) Molecule Y must have reacted to form the colourless solution as it's an alcohol *[1 mark]*. When alcohols are added to potassium manganate(VII), they are oxidised *[1 mark]* to form carboxylic acids *[1 mark]* (and the solution turns from purple to colourless). Molecule Z is an alkane, and so can't be oxidised by potassium manganate(VII) *[1 mark]*.
c)

[1 mark]

Pages 100-101 — Addition Polymerisation

1 a) B *[1 mark]*
b)

[1 mark]

c)

[1 mark]

d)

[1 mark]

2

[1 mark for a repeating unit that shows two carbon atoms with a single bond between them and 1 mark for correctly placed n on each side of the equation]

3 a) Selena, as the monomer contains a double bond between two carbon atoms / the monomer contains an alkene functional group *[1 mark]*.
b) B *[1 mark]*

Answers

Topic C6

Pages 102-103 — Condensation Polymerisation

1 a) Adenine, thymine, cytosine and guanine *[2 marks for all four correct, otherwise 1 mark for any 2 correct]*.

b) amino acid *[1 mark]*

2 a) This molecule can't form condensation polymers as monomers of condensation polymers must contain at least two reactive functional groups, with one at each end of the molecule *[1 mark]*. Propylamine only contains one functional group so cannot form condensation polymers *[1 mark]*.

b) A *[1 mark]*

3 a) a polyamide *[1 mark]*

b)

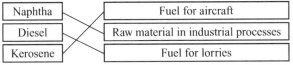

[1 mark for correct amide link, 1 mark for rest of diagram correct]

c) Carefully pour the solution in organic solvent on top of the solution in water without mixing them *[1 mark]*. Nylon-6,6 will be formed at the layer where the two solutions meet *[1 mark]*. Extract the nylon by slowly lifting it out of the beaker with a pair of tweezers *[1 mark]*. Collect the nylon as a thread by wrapping it around a rod as it's pulled from the beaker *[1 mark]*.

d) The industrial reaction will produce water (H_2O) as a by-product *[1 mark]*, whereas hydrochloric acid (HCl) will be produced in the lab reaction *[1 mark]*.

Pages 104-105 — Crude Oil

Warm–up

Naphtha	Fuel for aircraft
Diesel	Raw material in industrial processes
Kerosene	Fuel for lorries

(Naphtha → Raw material in industrial processes; Diesel → Fuel for lorries; Kerosene → Fuel for aircraft)

1 a) The remains of plants and animals are buried under a high temperature and pressure *[1 mark]* and, over millions of years, are turned into crude oil *[1 mark]*.

b) C_nH_{2n+2} *[1 mark]*

2 a) E.g. the population is increasing / less developed countries are becoming more developed *[1 mark for each correct answer, up to a maximum of 2]*.

b) Any two from: e.g. nuclear / wind / solar / ethanol / biodiesel *[1 mark for each correct answer]*.

c) Crude oil supplies are finite and non-renewable (so will one day run out) *[1 mark]*.

3 a) Oil is heated until most has turned to gas *[1 mark]*. The gases enter a fraction column which has a temperature gradient *[1 mark]*. The fractions separate out as longer hydrocarbons with high boiling points turn to liquid and drain out near the bottom of the column *[1 mark]*, while shorter hydrocarbons with lower boiling points turn to liquid and drain out near the top of the column *[1 mark]*.

b) i) LPG *[1 mark]*

ii) Any one from: e.g. oil / diesel / kerosene/paraffin / naphtha / petrol / bitumen *[1 mark]*.

c) i) triacontane *[1 mark]*

ii) E.g. The further down the column a fraction is collected, the higher its boiling point *[1 mark]*. Long hydrocarbons, like triacontane, have higher boiling points than shorter hydrocarbons like heptane *[1 mark]*. This is because their chains are much longer and there are many more intermolecular forces to break / the intermolecular bonding is stronger *[1 mark]*. More energy is needed to overcome these forces and turn them into a gas *[1 mark]*, so triacontane will have a higher boiling point than heptane and so triacontane will be collected further down the column *[1 mark]*.

Page 106 — Cracking

1 a) The amount of some fractions produced does not always meet the demand for those products *[1 mark]*. More of the product can be produced by cracking longer molecules into smaller, more useful ones *[1 mark]*.

b) powdered aluminium oxide *[1 mark]*

c) $C_{20}H_{42}$ *[1 mark]*

2 a) LPG *[1 mark]* and petrol and naphtha *[1 mark]*.

b) Oil and bitumen molecules can be cracked to produce extra diesel to help meet the demand *[1 mark]*.

Page 107 — Fuel Cells

1 a) A fuel cell is an electrical cell that is supplied with a fuel and oxygen *[1 mark]* and uses energy from the reaction between them to produce electrical energy *[1 mark]*.

b) B *[1 mark]*

2 a) E.g. phosphoric acid *[1 mark]*

b) At the cathode, oxygen gains electrons and reacts with H^+ ions (from the electrolyte) to produce water *[1 mark]*. This is a reduction reaction *[1 mark]*. At the anode, hydrogen loses electrons to produce H^+ ions *[1 mark]*. This is an oxidation reaction *[1 mark]*.

These reactions happen simultaneously, so the reaction is a redox reaction.

c) i) Any one from: e.g. it's expensive to adapt our current technology to run off fuel cells / hydrogen is difficult to extract / hydrogen is difficult to store *[1 mark]*.

ii) Hydrogen-oxygen fuel cells do produce a waste chemical, water *[1 mark]*. Clean water, as produced by fuel cells, is a useful and non-polluting chemical, so isn't a reason not to use fuel cells *[1 mark]*.

Page 108 — The Atmosphere

1 C *[1 mark]*

2 a) i) carbon dioxide *[1 mark]*

ii) Any two from, e.g: plants evolved which removed carbon dioxide through photosynthesis / carbon dioxide was locked in fossil fuels/sedimentary rocks / carbon dioxide dissolved in the oceans *[1 mark for each correct answer]*.

b) As green plants photosynthesised, they removed carbon dioxide and produced oxygen *[1 mark]*. There is hardly any oxygen present in Mars' atmosphere as there are no plants/no discovered life on Mars *[1 mark]*.

c) i) nitrogen *[1 mark]*

ii) Nitrogen was produced by ammonia reacting with oxygen *[1 mark]* and denitrifying bacteria *[1 mark]*. It built up in the atmosphere as it isn't very reactive so didn't break down *[1 mark]*.

Pages 109-110 — The Greenhouse Effect and Global Warming

Warm-up

Walking to school

Installing solar panels at home

1 D *[1 mark]*

2 a) An atmospheric gas that absorbs and reflects heat radiation *[1 mark]*.

b) E.g. methane / water vapour *[1 mark for each correct answer, up to a maximum of 2]*

c) Elvis is incorrect. The greenhouse effect is important as it keeps the Earth warm enough to support life *[1 mark]*.

d) Any two from: e.g. severe flooding / changing rainfall patterns / melting polar ice caps *[1 mark for each correct answer]*.

Answers

Mixed Questions

3 a)   How to grade your answer:
       Level 0:   There is no relevant information. *[No marks]*
       Level 1:   There is a brief explanation of what the data in the graph shows, but the conclusions drawn are brief and uncertainty is not discussed. *[1 to 2 marks]*
       Level 2:   There is a correct explanation of what the data in the graph shows and correct conclusions are drawn. There is some mention of the uncertainty associated with the conclusions. *[3 to 4 marks]*
       Level 3:   There is a clear and detailed conclusion of what the data in the graph shows, and the uncertainty associated with this data is thoroughly discussed. *[5 to 6 marks]*

Here are some points your answer may include:
The data in the graph shows that CO_2 emissions in the UK have decreased from the 1993 through to 2013.
The data shows that sea levels have risen from the 1993 through to 2013.
The data suggests that CO_2 emissions are not the cause of rising sea levels as the CO_2 emissions in the UK decrease as the sea level rises.
The data suggests that rising sea levels may not be anthropogenic.
The CO_2 emissions from burning fossil fuels are only from one country and are not a global figure.
The global CO_2 emissions from burning fossil fuels may be increasing so there could be a link between CO_2 emissions and a rise in sea levels.
CO_2 emissions from other sources, not just burning fossil fuels, should be considered.

b)   Any two from: e.g. encouraging energy efficiency / creating financial incentives to reduce CO_2 emissions / using more renewable energy / increasing research into new energy sources
[1 mark for each correct answer, up to a maximum of 2].

Page 111 — Pollutants

1 a)   Carbon monoxide stops blood from carrying oxygen around the body *[1 mark]*. The lack of oxygen can cause fainting, a coma or death *[1 mark]*.
  b)   A *[1 mark]*
2 a)   City A, as there are high levels of particulate carbon here *[1 mark]*. Particulate carbon, once it's escaped into the atmosphere, will eventually fall back to the ground as a black deposit which can coat buildings *[1 mark]*.
  b)   Any two from: e.g. breathing difficulties / headaches / tiredness *[1 mark for each correct answer]*.
  c)   City B, as it has the highest levels of nitrogen dioxide and sulfur dioxide *[1 mark]*. These pollutants mix with clouds and form dilute nitric and sulfuric acids, which fall as acid rain and can damage limestone buildings *[1 mark]*.

Page 112 — Water Treatment

1   D *[1 mark]*
2 a)   It is added to the water and makes fine particles clump together and settle at the bottom *[1 mark]*.
  b)   Chlorine gas is bubbled through the water to kill harmful bacteria and other microbes *[1 mark]*.
3 a)   Kuwait distils seawater as a source of drinking water as it has a low annual rainfall *[1 mark]*, so groundwater and surface water are unlikely to be readily available / seawater is likely to be the most accessible water *[1 mark]*.
  b)   Any one from: e.g. it requires lots of energy / it's expensive / it's impractical *[1 mark]*.

Mixed Questions

Pages 113-124 — Mixed Questions

1   B *[1 mark]*
2 a)   carboxylic acids *[1 mark]*
  b)   butanoic acid *[1 mark]*
  c) $M_r = (4 \times A_r \text{ of C}) + (8 \times A_r \text{ of H}) + (2 \times A_r \text{ of O})$
       $= (4 \times 12.0) + (8 \times 1.0) + (2 \times 16.0)$
       $= 48.0 + 8.0 + 32.0 = \mathbf{88.0}$
       [2 marks for the correct answer, otherwise 1 mark for an expression which could be correctly evaluated to give the M_r of butanoic acid]
  d)   molecular formula = $C_4H_8O_2$
       The largest number that all the numbers in the molecular formula will divide by is 2:
       C: $4 \div 2 = 2$
       H: $8 \div 2 = 4$
       O: $2 \div 2 = 1$
       So the empirical formula is $\mathbf{C_2H_4O}$ *[1 mark]*
3 a)   Name: lithium bromide *[1 mark]*
       Formula: LiBr *[1 mark]*
  b)   7 *[1 mark]*
  c) i) E.g. To test for Li^+ ions, dip a clean wire loop in the solution, then put the loop in the clear blue part of a Bunsen flame. If Li^+ ions are present, a crimson/red flame will be seen *[1 mark for describing a valid test for Li^+ ions, 1 mark for describing the observation expected if Li^+ ions are present]*.
     ii) E.g. To test for Br^- ions, add some dilute nitric acid, then a few drops of silver nitrate solution. If Br^- ions are present, a cream precipitate will form *[1 mark for describing a valid test for Br^- ions, 1 mark for describing the observation expected if Br^- ions are present]*.
4 a) $Ca + Cu(NO_3)_2 \rightarrow Ca(NO_3)_2 + Cu$
       [2 marks for all formulas correct and a correctly-balanced equation, otherwise 1 mark for correct formulas in an unbalanced equation]
  b)   Oxidising agent: copper
       Reducing agent: calcium *[1 mark]*
The copper goes from being a 2+ ion to having no charge as copper metal, so it gains electrons. That means copper is reduced, so calcium is the reducing agent. Similarly, calcium is oxidised by copper, so copper is the oxidising agent.
5 a) i) E.g. burning of sulfur impurities in fossil fuels *[1 mark for a valid source of SO_2 pollution]*.
     ii) SO_2 mixes with clouds to form sulfuric acid, causing acid rain *[1 mark]*.
  b) $2SO_2 + O_2 \rightleftharpoons 2SO_3$
       [2 marks for all formulas correct and a correctly-balanced equation, otherwise 1 mark for correct formulas in an unbalanced equation]
This is a reversible reaction, so it should have a reversible $\rightleftharpoons$ arrow — but you'd get the marks here if you got everything else right and put a normal $\rightarrow$ arrow instead.
6 a) i) oxygen / O_2 *[1 mark]*
     ii) hydrogen / H_2 *[1 mark]*
  b) i) The metal is more reactive than hydrogen *[1 mark]*.
     ii) The non-metal ion is not a halide ion *[1 mark]*.
7 a)   E.g. both can conduct electricity as solid metals have delocalised electrons which can carry a charge *[1 mark for any common property of metals not mentioned in the table, 1 mark for an explanation relating that property to metallic bonding]*.
  b)   Any two from e.g. transition metals and their compounds make good catalysts / they usually form more than one ion / they form colourful compounds / they are relatively unreactive *[1 mark for each property. No marks for*

Answers

properties common to metals in general, e.g. hard, strong, shiny, heat/electrical conductors].

c) E.g. the cups would need to be lightweight, as campers might want to carry them long distances in their bags, tough enough not to break easily when being packed or carried in bags, and cheap to manufacture. Glass would not be suitable, as it is very brittle, so would break easily. Titanium would be too expensive, and is also the heaviest of the four materials. Duralumin would be unsuitable because it corrodes and is also quite heavy. Melamine resin is more brittle than most of the others, but would be most suitable, because it's fairly tough, lightweight and cheap.
[1 mark for each valid comparison between properties from the table, up to a total of 3 marks. 1 mark for choosing a material and giving suitable justification of the choice.]

8 a) $2Rb + F_2 \rightarrow 2RbF$
[2 marks for all formulas correct and a correctly-balanced equation, otherwise 1 mark for correct formulas in an unbalanced equation]

b) ionic *[1 mark]*

c) The compound will have a high melting point, because there are strong forces of electrostatic attraction between the ions *[1 mark]* and a large amount of energy is needed to overcome these forces and melt the solid *[1 mark]*.

9 a) The solution would change from colourless to brown *[1 mark]*.

b) Chlorine is more reactive than iodine *[1 mark]*, so it displaces iodine from the potassium iodide solution *[1 mark]*.

c) $Cl_2 + 2I^- \rightarrow 2Cl^- + I_2$
[1 mark for correct left-hand side, 1 mark for correct right-hand side]

d) Chlorine: $Cl_2 + 2e^- \rightarrow 2Cl^-$ *[1 mark]*
Iodine: $2I^- \rightarrow I_2 + 2e^-$ *[1 mark]*

10 C *[1 mark]*
The smaller cubes will give the highest rate of reaction, as they have the greatest surface area to volume ratio.

11 a) Aluminium is reduced and oxygen is oxidised *[1 mark]*.

b) Solid bauxite can't be electrolysed as the ions are in fixed positions and can't move *[1 mark]*. When bauxite is molten, the ions are free to move and conduct electricity *[1 mark]*.

c) Heating with carbon will only reduce metals that are less reactive than carbon *[1 mark]*. Aluminium is more reactive than carbon, so heating with carbon will not extract aluminium metal from its ore *[1 mark]*.

d) Any two from: e.g. Recycling reduces waste going to landfill. / Recycling requires less energy than extracting aluminium from its ore. / Recycling is cheaper than extracting aluminium from its ore. / Recycling reduces the need to mine aluminium ore, so it therefore reduces damage to the landscape caused by mining. / Recycling preserves natural resources, so it is more sustainable.
[1 mark for each valid advantage]

12 a)

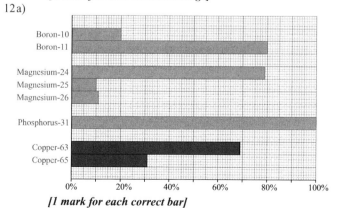

[1 mark for each correct bar]

b) The relative atomic mass of an element is the average of the mass numbers of all the atoms of that element *[1 mark]*. Phosphorus only has one isotope, so its relative atomic mass is equal to the mass number of its atoms (31) *[1 mark]*. Boron, magnesium and copper all have more than one isotope, which exist in different quantities, so the average of their mass numbers won't be a whole number *[1 mark]*.

c) 20% of boron atoms are boron-10, so in 1 mole of boron atoms, the number of boron-10 atoms = $6.022 \times 10^{23} \times 0.2$ = 1.2044×10^{23} = 1.20×10^{23} atoms to 3 s.f.
[1 mark for a correct answer, 1 mark for correctly rounding to 3 s.f.]

d) The atomic number is equal to the number of electrons in an atom *[1 mark]*, and 2+ ions are formed when the atom loses 2 electrons, so an Mg^{2+} ion contains $12 - 2 = 10$ electrons *[1 mark]*.

13 a) $BaCl_2(aq) + 2AgNO_3(aq) \rightarrow 2AgCl(s) + Ba(NO_3)_2(aq)$
[1 mark]

b) i) Crystallisation is used to separate soluble solids from solutions *[1 mark]*, so if he tried to separate the reaction mixture using crystallisation, Andre would end up with a mixture of solid silver chloride and solid barium nitrate *[1 mark]*.

ii) filtration *[1 mark]*

c) M_r of AgCl = A_r of Ag + A_r of Cl = $107.9 + 35.5 = 143.4$
[1 mark]
M_r of $Ba(NO_3)_2 = A_r$ of Ba + $[2 \times (A_r$ of N + $(3 \times A_r$ of O))]$
= $137.3 + [2 \times (14.0 + (3 \times 16.0))]$
= $137.3 + [2 \times (14.0 + 48.0)]$
= $137.3 + [2 \times 62.0]$
= $137.3 + 124.0 = 261.3$ *[1 mark]*
Atom economy
= (M_r of desired products ÷ M_r of all products) × 100
= (($2 \times M_r$ of AgCl) ÷ (($2 \times M_r$ of AgCl) + M_r of $Ba(NO_3)_2$)) × 100
= ((2×143.4) ÷ ((2×143.4) + 261.3)) × 100
= (286.8 ÷ ($286.8 + 261.3$)) × 100
= ($286.8 ÷ 548.1$) × 100
= $52.3262...$ = **52.3%** (to 3 s.f.)
[3 marks for calculating 52.3262..., plus 1 mark for correctly rounding to 3 significant figures. Otherwise 1 mark for calculating M_r of both products, 1 mark for correct method for finding atom economy.]

d) number of moles in 33.98 g of $AgNO_3$
= mass ÷ (M_r of $AgNO_3$)
= $33.98 ÷ [107.9 + 14.0 + (3 \times 16.0)]$
= $33.98 ÷ [107.9 + 14.0 + 48.0]$
= $33.98 ÷ 169.9 = 0.2$
2 moles of $AgNO_3$ produces 2 moles of AgCl,
so 0.2 moles of $AgNO_3$ produces 0.2 moles of AgCl.
Theoretical yield = mass of 0.2 moles of AgCl
= $0.2 \times M_r$ of AgCl = $0.2 \times (107.9 + 35.5)$
= $0.2 \times 143.4 = 28.68$
So percentage yield
= (actual yield ÷ theoretical yield) × 100
= ($21.51 ÷ 28.68$) × 100
= **75%**
[5 marks for correct answer, otherwise 1 mark for calculating number of moles in 33.98 g of $AgNO_3$, 1 mark for correct method to find the number of moles of AgCl that should be produced, 1 mark for correct method to calculate theoretical yield in grams, 1 mark for correct method to calculate percentage yield.]

14 B *[1 mark]*

Mixed Questions

15a) The reaction is reversible *[1 mark]*.

b) How to grade your answer:

Level 0: There is no relevant information. *[No marks]*

Level 1: Some understanding of the effects of temperature and pressure on the equilibrium is shown, but not all the factors in the question are correctly addressed. *[1 to 2 marks]*

Level 2: Understanding of the effects of temperature and pressure on the equilibrium is shown, and the reasons why **one** of the conditions is considered a compromise are clearly and correctly explained. *[3 to 4 marks]*

Level 3: Understanding of the effects of temperature and pressure on the equilibrium is shown, and the reasons why **both** the conditions are considered compromises are clearly and correctly explained. *[5 to 6 marks]*

Here are some points your answer may include:

The reaction equation has fewer gas moles on the products side, so higher pressures favour the forward reaction.

Higher pressure also increases the rate of reaction.

Higher pressures will give a greater yield of ammonia, but are more expensive to generate and maintain.

The pressure of 200 atm is a compromise between yield and cost.

The forward reaction is exothermic (it gives out heat), so lower temperatures favour the forward reaction.

A low temperature would give a high yield of ammonia, but low temperatures mean a lower rate of reaction.

At low temperatures the reaction would be too slow to generate a useful amount of ammonia.

The temperature of 450 °C is a compromise between the equilibrium position and the rate of reaction, because it generates ammonia quickly, even though it doesn't provide the maximum yield.

16a) B *[1 mark]*

b) Bonds broken:

$(2 \times H–H) + O=O = (2 \times 436) + 498$

$= 872 + 498 = 1370$ kJ/mol

Bonds formed:

$4 \times O–H = 4 \times 463 = 1852$ kJ/mol

Energy change = $1370 – 1852 =$ **–482 kJ/mol**

[3 marks for correct answer, otherwise 1 mark for correct energy value for bonds broken, 1 mark for correct energy value for bonds formed.]

c) Number of moles of H_2

= volume ÷ 24 = 156 ÷ 24 = 6.5 moles

From part b), 486 kJ of energy is produced when 2 moles of H_2 reacts, so total amount of energy released

= 6.5 × (486 ÷ 2) = 1579.5 kJ

[3 marks for the correct answer, otherwise 1 mark for calculating the number of moles of H_2 and 1 mark for a partly-correct method using the energy change from part b) and the number of moles of H_2. Allow full marks for using the correct method with an incorrect value from part b), but no other errors.]

17 Number of moles of aluminium used

= mass of aluminium used ÷ A_r of aluminium

= 162 ÷ 27.0 = 6 moles

3 moles of H_2 are produced for every 2 moles of Al used, so moles of H_2 produced = (6 ÷ 2) × 3 = 9 moles

volume = number of moles × 24

= 9 × 24 = **216 dm³**

[3 marks for correct answer, otherwise 1 mark for number of moles of aluminium used, 1 mark for number of moles of H_2 produced.]

18 Block X would react most quickly. Block X has the greatest surface area to volume ratio *[1 mark]*, and rate of reaction increases as surface area to volume ratio increases *[1 mark]*.

You don't actually need to work out the surface area to volume ratios here — all the blocks have the same volume, so the ratio must be greatest for the one with the greatest surface area.

19a) i) cubic

ii) hexagonal *[1 mark for parts i) and ii) both correct]*

b) Each atom is bonded to four other atoms with strong covalent bonds *[1 mark]*, which makes crystals of cubic boron nitride very rigid / hard *[1 mark]*.

c) The sheets of hexagonal boron nitride are held together by very weak forces *[1 mark]* so the layers are very slippery because they can slide easily over each other *[1 mark]*.

d) Hexagonal boron nitride does not contain any delocalised electrons *[1 mark]*.

ISBN 978 1 78294 521 5

9 781782 945215

CRQA41   £2.00
              (Retail Price)

www.cgpbooks.co.uk